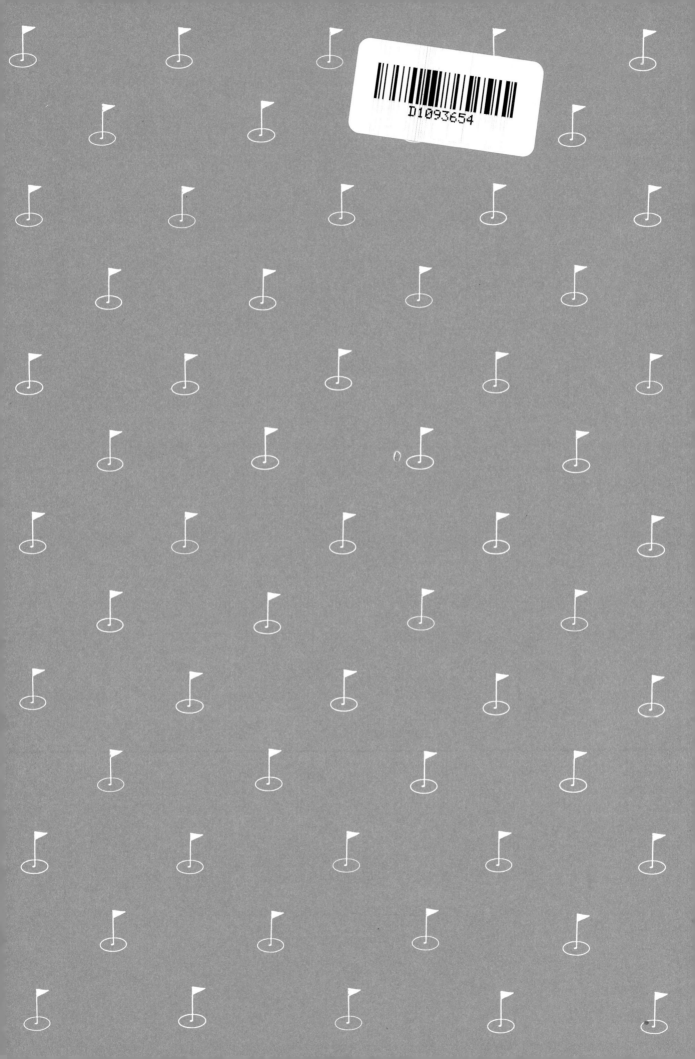

MY GOLFING RECORD

with an introduction by

PETER DOBEREINER

BRACKEN BOOKS
LONDON

My Golfing Record is published by Bracken Books,
a Division of Bestsellers Publications Limited,
Princess House, 50 Eastcastle Street,
London W1N 7AP, England

Printed in Spain

ISBN   1 85170 185 0

Produced for Bracken Books by
Morgan Samuel Editions,
4, Somerset Road, London W13 9PB

Illustrations courtesy of Sarah Baddiel, *Golfiana*

CONTENTS

INTRODUCTION

ON BEING ASKED to contribute an introduction to this volume
I must admit to feeling that it would be a struggle.

Imagine that you are the master of an early sailing ship. You are
thoroughly versed in the accumulated nautical wisdom of the ages
and so your first article of faith is that if you sail south the sea begins
to boil and unless you reverse your course your ship will shortly fall
over the edge of the world. That is the number one law of the sea.
Then the king sends for you and says: "I have a hunch that the earth
might well be round. Give it a try. Maintain your course and if my
hunch is right you will eventually arrive back here". I felt rather like
that captain when I was asked to contribute an introduction for this
volume. My instincts were less than sympathetic.

After all, what golfer would solemnly sit down after a round of
golf and record every detail? Really! The correct form after a
memorable round is to proceed directly to the bar and order doubles
all round. In a well conducted club the subsequent proceedings erases
all details of the golf from the memory. Then, as I sat in my
accustomed pose of a blank mind confronting a blank sheet of paper
my eye fell on a framed 20 escudo note bearing a slightly vulgar
inscription by Henry Cotton, a momento of the one occasion my
latent talents had prevailed over the Master. When was that?
Obviously it was in Portugal, but which course? What was the result
and how were the figures? I wished I could remember and then I
wished I had made some kind of note about our match. Once those
pangs of regret start nagging at you they tend to get worse. What
about the time I made a concerted attack on the golf courses of
Ireland? There were two of us in a car and we averaged better than
two courses a day for a fortnight.

But where did we start? Where did we finish? At this range of time I cannot begin to recall which courses we played. The memory is hopelessly fogged, those adventures lost beyond recall. And then, I am reminded, there was the occasion when I perpetrated a gross folly and accepted a magazine commission to list in order of merit the 50 greatest courses outside America. To my astonishment quite a number of golfers wrote to me saying that they had been inspired to devote all their vacations for as long as it took to playing all 50 courses. I do hope they all made it and that they recorded their adventures and impressions of every course. A book like this would have been the perfect medium to preserve the experience of a lifetime. Golf holidays are one obvious use, as are pro-ams, club competitions and noteworthy rounds of social golf. There is a theory that golfers get too caught up in the outcome of their bets and the technical problems of their swings to enjoy the game while they are actually playing it; the true satisfactions of golf are in anticipation of the virtuosity you are going to display next time and in reflection on past triumphs. In that case the keeping of records must add to the pleasure of golf because, as I can attest, the joys of anticipation fade with age and all you are left with are reflections.

Peter Dobereiner

MY PERSONAL FILE

I learned my golf: _____

_____

_____

_____

My local club: _____

_____

_____

Phone no: _____

Professional: _____

Phone no: _____

Executive office / Secretary: _____

Phone no: _____

My vacation club: _____

_____

_____

Phone no: _____

Professional: _____

Phone no: _____

Executive office / Secretary: _____

Phone no: _____

My vacation club: _____

_____

_____

Phone no: _____

Professional: _____

Phone no: _____

Executive office / Secretary: _____

Phone no: _____

©

MY GOLFING EQUIPMENT

Woods: Model No.   Manufacturer   Date Purchased

_____

_____

_____

_____

_____

_____

_____

Irons: Model No.   Manufacturer   Date Purchased

_____

_____

_____

_____

_____

_____

_____

_____

_____

_____

_____

Putters: Model No.   Manufacturer   Date Purchased

_____

_____

Miscellaneous:

_____

_____

©

HANDICAP RECORD

Date	Handicap	Date	Handicap	Date	Handicap
_____	_____	_____	_____	_____	_____
_____	_____	_____	_____	_____	_____
_____	_____	_____	_____	_____	_____
_____	_____	_____	_____	_____	_____
_____	_____	_____	_____	_____	_____
_____	_____	_____	_____	_____	_____

Date	Handicap	Date	Handicap	Date	Handicap
_____	_____	_____	_____	_____	_____
_____	_____	_____	_____	_____	_____
_____	_____	_____	_____	_____	_____
_____	_____	_____	_____	_____	_____
_____	_____	_____	_____	_____	_____
_____	_____	_____	_____	_____	_____

Date	Handicap	Date	Handicap	Date	Handicap
_____	_____	_____	_____	_____	_____
_____	_____	_____	_____	_____	_____
_____	_____	_____	_____	_____	_____
_____	_____	_____	_____	_____	_____
_____	_____	_____	_____	_____	_____
_____	_____	_____	_____	_____	_____

Date	Handicap	Date	Handicap	Date	Handicap
_____	_____	_____	_____	_____	_____
_____	_____	_____	_____	_____	_____
_____	_____	_____	_____	_____	_____
_____	_____	_____	_____	_____	_____
_____	_____	_____	_____	_____	_____

Date	Handicap	Date	Handicap	Date	Handicap
___	___	___	___	___	___
___	___	___	___	___	___
___	___	___	___	___	___
___	___	___	___	___	___
___	___	___	___	___	___
___	___	___	___	___	___

Date	Handicap	Date	Handicap	Date	Handicap
___	___	___	___	___	___
___	___	___	___	___	___
___	___	___	___	___	___
___	___	___	___	___	___
___	___	___	___	___	___
___	___	___	___	___	___

Date	Handicap	Date	Handicap	Date	Handicap
___	___	___	___	___	___
___	___	___	___	___	___
___	___	___	___	___	___
___	___	___	___	___	___
___	___	___	___	___	___
___	___	___	___	___	___

Date	Handicap	Date	Handicap	Date	Handicap
___	___	___	___	___	___
___	___	___	___	___	___
___	___	___	___	___	___
___	___	___	___	___	___
___	___	___	___	___	___
___	___	___	___	___	___

©

My Golfing Highlights

– a record of my triumphs in competition

Competition:_____
Course:_____ Date:_____
Score:_____ Prize:_____
Remarks:_____
_____

Competition:_____
Course:_____ Date:_____
Score:_____ Prize:_____
Remarks:_____
_____

Competition:_____
Course:_____ Date:_____
Score:_____ Prize:_____
Remarks:_____
_____

Competition:_____
Course:_____ Date:_____
Score:_____ Prize:_____
Remarks:_____
_____

Competition:_____
Course:_____ Date:_____
Score:_____ Prize:_____
Remarks:_____
_____

©

– a record of my triumphs in competition

Competition:_____
Course:_____ Date:_____
Score:_____ Prize:_____
Remarks:_____
_____

Competition:_____
Course:_____ Date:_____
Score:_____ Prize:_____
Remarks:_____
_____

Competition:_____
Course:_____ Date:_____
Score:_____ Prize:_____
Remarks:_____
_____

Competition:_____
Course:_____ Date:_____
Score:_____ Prize:_____
Remarks:_____
_____

Competition:_____
Course:_____ Date:_____
Score:_____ Prize:_____
Remarks:_____
_____

ROUND REPORT

Date: _____

Course: _____

Time started: _____ Time finished: _____

Weather: _____

Players: _____ Strokes received: _____

        _____   _____

        _____   _____

        _____   _____

        _____   _____

Competition details:

Singles:	_____		Greensome:	_____
Foursomes:	_____		Stableford:	_____
3-ball:	_____		Stroke-play:	_____
4-ball:	_____		Match-play:	_____

Stakes: _____

Best hole: _____
_____

Best shot: _____
_____

Incidents: _____
_____
_____
_____

Result: _____
_____
_____
_____

©

"The golfer's wardrobe needs a little thought. Golfing garments ought to be made of materials which will stand in all weathers, and, above all, shoes should be strong and waterproof, and stockings should be of pure wool. By far the most serviceable kind of skirt is still the never-out-of-fashion tweed! There is one thing about a good Harris or Donegal tweed: it lasts for ages and keeps its cut to its last days. Bright-coloured sports coats and woollen polo jumpers always look well on the golf course."

HOME CHATS, April 1925

MENS' OFFICIAL COURSE	PAR											
	DISTANCE											
	HANDICAP/STROKE INDEX											
A												
B												
	HOLE	1	2	3	4	5	6	7	8	9	OUT
C												
D												
MATCHES												
LADIES' OFFICIAL COURSE	HANDICAP/STROKE INDEX											
	DISTANCE											
	PAR											

										REPAIR BALL MARKS	
10	11	12	13	14	15	16	17	18	IN	TOTAL	HDCP	NET
										REPLACE DIVOTS	
SCORER		ATTESTED			DATE						

©

ROUND REPORT

Date: _____

Course: _____

Time started: _____ Time finished: _____

Weather: _____

Players: _____ Strokes received: _____

        _____   _____

        _____   _____

        _____   _____

        _____   _____

Competition details:

Singles:	_____	Greensome:	_____
Foursomes:	_____	Stableford:	_____
3-ball:	_____	Stroke-play:	_____
4-ball:	_____	Match-play:	_____

Stakes: _____

Best hole: _____

_____

Best shot: _____

_____

Incidents: _____

_____

_____

_____

Result: _____

_____

_____

_____

©

"I trust readers will not arrive at the conclusion that I am advocating wagering on golf matches. I cannot call it gambling, as such wagers as take place are in far too mild a form to come within that category, but I have found in the past that there are uncharitable people in this world who are only to willing to pounce upon any little shred of evidence to arrive at erroneous conclusions and make unpleasant remarks, invariably under the cloak of anonymity. As I said before, it would be idle to shut one's eyes to the fact that there is a certain amount of wagering in connection with the game, and it undoubtedly has the object of giving an added interest to many whose golfing ability is not equal to the task of taking a prominent part in the competition itself."

THE IRISH GOLFER, March 1902

MENS' OFFICIAL COURSE	PAR											
	DISTANCE											
	HANDICAP/STROKE INDEX											
A												
B												
	HOLE	1	2	3	4	5	6	7	8	9	OUT
C												
D												
MATCHES												
LADIES' OFFICIAL COURSE	HANDICAP/STROKE INDEX											
	DISTANCE											
	PAR											

											REPAIR BALL MARKS	
10	11	12	13	14	15	16	17	18	IN	TOTAL	HDCP	NET
											REPLACE DIVOTS	
SCORER		ATTESTED			DATE		

©

ROUND REPORT

Date: _____

Course: _____

Time started: _____ Time finished: _____

Weather: _____

Players: _____ Strokes received: _____

            _____   _____

            _____   _____

            _____   _____

            _____   _____

Competition details:

Singles:	_____	Greensome:	_____
Foursomes:	_____	Stableford:	_____
3-ball:	_____	Stroke-play:	_____
4-ball:	_____	Match-play:	_____

Stakes: _____

Best hole: _____

_____

Best shot: _____

_____

Incidents: _____

_____

_____

_____

Result: _____

_____

_____

_____

©

16

"You stride away half breathless over the short crisp grass, cut close by the winds as neatly as by a mowing machine, your eyes fixed on the balls flying far before you, or on the demonstrative figure of the boy sent in advance to mark them, as his ragged figure changes itself into an animated telegraph. Your friendly adversary is moving in a parallel line, at the moment in his intense excitement contorting his person into an ungainly wriggle in sympathy with his ball, which a gust of wind is just twisting towards a patch of furze. It lights there, and his tattered follower who, with slight garments and blue pinched face, is shivering along under his armful of clubs, slaps his gaunt thigh despairingly in an access of eloquent sympathy; while your own attendant chuckles confidentially into your ear his jubilation over your enemy's grief."

THE PALL MALL GAZETTE, November 1868.

MENS' OFFICIAL COURSE	PAR										
	DISTANCE										
	HANDICAP/STROKE INDEX										
A											
B											
HOLE		1	2	3	4	5	6	7	8	9	OUT
C											
D											
MATCHES											
LADIES' OFFICIAL COURSE	HANDICAP/STROKE INDEX										
	DISTANCE										
	PAR										

										REPAIR BALL MARKS	
10	11	12	13	14	15	16	17	18	IN	TOTAL	HDCP	NET
											REPLACE DIVOTS	
SCORER		ATTESTED			DATE							

ROUND REPORT

Date: _____

Course: _____

Time started: _____ Time finished: _____

Weather: _____

Players: _____ Strokes received: _____

    _____   _____

    _____   _____

    _____   _____

    _____   _____

Competition details:

Singles:	_____	Greensome:	_____
Foursomes:	_____	Stableford:	_____
3-ball:	_____	Stroke-play:	_____
4-ball:	_____	Match-play:	_____

Stakes: _____

Best hole: _____

_____

Best shot: _____

_____

Incidents: _____

_____

_____

_____

Result: _____

_____

_____

_____

"The story of the birth and rapid growth of the game in this country should not in these first years of its existence be overlooked. There are today, at a conservative estimate, some seventy-five clubs in the United States which maintain golf links ... The St Andrews Club was incorporated in 1888, the Shinnecock Hills Club in 1890; but amongst nearly all the other clubs, the game is hardly more than a year or two old. Yet has already been established upon a firm foundation and given recognition by the organization of a National Golfing Association; and with the stimulus which this association will surely give, the coming summer will certainly see the game branching out in every direction."

GOLF IN AMERICA, 1895

MENS' OFFICIAL COURSE	PAR										
	DISTANCE										
	HANDICAP / STROKE INDEX										
A											
B											
	HOLE	1	2	3	4	5	6	7	8	9	OUT
C											
D											
MATCHES											
LADIES' OFFICIAL COURSE	HANDICAP / STROKE INDEX										
	DISTANCE										
	PAR										

										REPAIR BALL MARKS	
10	11	12	13	14	15	16	17	18	IN	TOTAL	HDCP	NET
											REPLACE DIVOTS	
SCORER		ATTESTED		DATE							

©

ROUND REPORT

Date: _____

Course: _____

Time started: _____ Time finished: _____

Weather: _____

Players: _____ Strokes received: _____

_____ _____

_____ _____

_____ _____

_____ _____

Competition details:

Singles: _____ Greensome: _____

Foursomes: _____ Stableford: _____

3-ball: _____ Stroke-play: _____

4-ball: _____ Match-play: _____

Stakes: _____

Best hole: _____

_____

Best shot: _____

_____

Incidents: _____

_____

_____

_____

Result: _____

_____

_____

_____

©

"Ah well. I picked up this cleek, from a boy who wanted to sell, for $1.25. It was the first club I ever owned, back in 1897. It was my full set. It was the club with which I shot a score of 21 round the caddie course at the Walworth County Country Club. The record was 19, for five holes ... It weighs 14.5 ounces, has a 38-inch hickory shaft, a blade four inches long, with a depth at the centre of 1.25 inches.

Sometimes, my dear Grantland, I think, with our marvellous modern development of clubs, stepped up ten yards at a step, and a lively ball that travels so far, we have lost a little something in golf, especially when I remember how Harry Vardon with six clubs played six consecutive rounds of 68 or better. Perhaps that may have been because Vardon was an artist and not an artisan."

OB Keeler, THE AMERICAN GOLFER, 1932

MENS' OFFICIAL COURSE	PAR										
	DISTANCE										
	HANDICAP/STROKE INDEX										
A											
B											
	HOLE	1	2	3	4	5	6	7	8	9	OUT
C											
D											
MATCHES											
LADIES' OFFICIAL COURSE	HANDICAP/STROKE INDEX										
	DISTANCE										
	PAR										

										REPAIR BALL MARKS	
10	11	12	13	14	15	16	17	18	IN	TOTAL	HDCP	NET
											REPLACE DIVOTS	
SCORER			ATTESTED			DATE						

©

ROUND REPORT

Date: _____

Course: _____

Time started: _____ Time finished: _____

Weather: _____

Players: _____ Strokes received: _____

_____ _____

_____ _____

_____ _____

_____ _____

Competition details:

Singles:	_____		Greensome:	_____
Foursomes:	_____		Stableford:	_____
3-ball:	_____		Stroke-play:	_____
4-ball:	_____		Match-play:	_____

Stakes: _____

Best hole: _____

_____

Best shot: _____

_____

Incidents: _____

_____

_____

_____

Result: _____

_____

_____

©

"In conclusion, one may say that it is almost impossible to over-estimate the extra-ordinary improvement that has taken place in ladies' golf over the last three or four years. The game is now taken up thoroughly and seriously, and played in deadly earnest. Of course, the earnestness displayed by some very indifferent players over their utterly feeble performances would move the grimmest cynic to a smile of pity. But we have it on the highest authority that the population of these islands consists mostly of fools; so how can even the ranks of the elect (ie golfers) hope to escape a few stragglers from the great army of idiots? Thus a fool, hot and weary in a bunker, calls faintly "How many strokes have you played, dear?" "Twenty-seven, I think." "Oh! Then I give up the hole.""

BADMINTON MAGAZINE, 1898

MENS' OFFICIAL COURSE	PAR										
	DISTANCE										
	HANDICAP/STROKE INDEX										
A											
B											
	HOLE	1	2	3	4	5	6	7	8	9	OUT
C											
D											
MATCHES											
LADIES' OFFICIAL COURSE	HANDICAP/STROKE INDEX										
	DISTANCE										
	PAR										

									REPAIR BALL MARKS	
10	11	12	13	14	15	16	17	18	IN	TOTAL	HDCP	NET
										REPLACE DIVOTS	
SCORER		ATTESTED			DATE							

©

ROUND REPORT

Date:_____

Course:_____

Time started:_____ Time finished:_____

Weather:_____

Players: _____ Strokes received: _____

_____ _____

_____ _____

_____ _____

_____ _____

Competition details:

Singles:	_____	Greensome:	_____
Foursomes:	_____	Stableford:	_____
3-ball:	_____	Stroke-play:	_____
4-ball:	_____	Match-play:	_____

Stakes:_____

Best hole:_____

_____

Best shot:_____

_____

Incidents:_____

_____

_____

_____

Result:_____

_____

_____

_____

©

"There is such a thing as automatic golf. The muscles have a marvellous sense of their own – it is sometimes called psychology – by which they excite themselves for the job in hand. Take the matter of putting: it is quite probable that a large percentage of all good shots are executed with a quick look at the cup, and no thought whatever as to how hard to hit the ball. The idea in all golf strokes is to make the swing automatic from tee shot to putt. A good putter automatically develops the right habit. He develops the habit of concentration, one of the greatest habits in golf to have working for you. It is hard to make yourself concentrate by sheer mental force. But it is simple enough when it becomes automatic by force of habit."

John M Charlotte, GOLFING ILLUSTRATED, October 1925

MENS' OFFICIAL COURSE	PAR										
	DISTANCE										
	HANDICAP/STROKE INDEX										
A											
B											
	HOLE	1	2	3	4	5	6	7	8	9	OUT
C											
D											
MATCHES											
LADIES' OFFICIAL COURSE	HANDICAP/STROKE INDEX										
	DISTANCE										
	PAR										

									REPAIR BALL MARKS	
10	11	12	13	14	15	16	17	18	IN	TOTAL	HDCP	NET
											REPLACE DIVOTS	
SCORER		ATTESTED			DATE							

©

ROUND REPORT

Date: _____

Course: _____

Time started: _____ Time finished: _____

Weather: _____

Players: _____ Strokes received: _____

    _____   _____

    _____   _____

    _____   _____

    _____   _____

Competition details:

    Singles: _____   Greensome: _____

    Foursomes: _____   Stableford: _____

    3-ball: _____   Stroke-play: _____

    4-ball: _____   Match-play: _____

Stakes: _____

Best hole: _____

_____

Best shot: _____

_____

Incidents: _____

_____

_____

_____

Result: _____

_____

_____

_____

©

"The Myopia Hunt Club of Wenham, famous in polo and hunting annuals, is an admirable golfing land, with good distances, natural hazards, commanding extensive views of the adjoining country, where the whistle of the quail tickles the sportsman's ear, and the music of the kennelled hounds testifies to the various sports of its members.

At the last hole is a pond in whose depths lies a hidden treasure of golf balls, and over whose surface has been wafted many a smothered and unsmothered curse. The story is told of one enthusiastic tyro who drove two or three balls into the water, and sent his caddie to the clubhouse for a fresh supply; then, opening the box, he drove the whole dozen into the pond. Such exhibitions are common to the game, and a great relief to the surcharged heart."

SCRIBNER'S MAGAZINE, May 1895

MENS' OFFICIAL COURSE	PAR										
	DISTANCE										
	HANDICAP/STROKE INDEX										
A											
B											
	HOLE	1	2	3	4	5	6	7	8	9	OUT
C											
D											
MATCHES											
LADIES' OFFICIAL COURSE	HANDICAP/STROKE INDEX										
	DISTANCE										
	PAR										

									REPAIR BALL MARKS	
10	11	12	13	14	15	16	17	18	IN	TOTAL	HDCP	NET
										REPLACE DIVOTS	

SCORER	ATTESTED	DATE

©

ROUND REPORT

Date: _____

Course: _____

Time started: _____ Time finished: _____

Weather: _____

Players: _____ Strokes received: _____

                 _____   _____

                 _____   _____

                 _____   _____

                 _____   _____

Competition details:

	Singles:	_____		Greensome:	_____
	Foursomes:	_____		Stableford:	_____
	3-ball:	_____		Stroke-play:	_____
	4-ball:	_____		Match-play:	_____

Stakes: _____

Best hole: _____

_____

Best shot: _____

_____

Incidents: _____

_____

_____

_____

Result: _____

_____

_____

_____

©

"It is, of course, notorious that the player who is permitted under the terms of his handicap to shout "Boo!" in the ear of an opponent three times in the course of a round, just as the unfortunate man is addressing his ball, possesses an advantage which should always enable him to secure the match.

The right to "Boo!" need never, as a matter of fact, be exercised, the mere knowledge that this exclamation is perpetually dangling like the sword of Damocles over his head being as a rule quite sufficient to put the most experienced player off his game. With 18 bisques and a couple of "Boo's!" I should be quite ready to challenge Vardon himself."

Harry Graham, THE COMPLETE SPORTSMAN, 1919

MENS' OFFICIAL COURSE	PAR										
	DISTANCE										
	HANDICAP/STROKE INDEX										
A											
B											
	HOLE	1	2	3	4	5	6	7	8	9	OUT
C											
D											
MATCHES											
LADIES' OFFICIAL COURSE	HANDICAP/STROKE INDEX										
	DISTANCE										
	PAR										

									REPAIR BALL MARKS	
10	11	12	13	14	15	16	17	18	IN	TOTAL	HDCP	NET
										REPLACE DIVOTS	

SCORER   ATTESTED   DATE

©

ROUND REPORT

Date:_____

Course:_____

Time started:_____ Time finished:_____

Weather:_____

Players:_____ Strokes received:_____

    _____   _____

    _____   _____

    _____   _____

    _____   _____

Competition details:

Singles:	_____	Greensome:	_____
Foursomes:	_____	Stableford:	_____
3-ball:	_____	Stroke-play:	_____
4-ball:	_____	Match-play:	_____

Stakes:_____

Best hole:_____

_____

Best shot:_____

_____

Incidents:_____

_____

_____

_____

Result:_____

_____

_____

_____

© \

"I am thoroughly convinced that the great secret of the long and straight shot with the wooden clubs is in delivering the blow "late". By "late" I mean delivering the blow at and through the ball. This phrase means directing the mind, and calling up every atom of physical energy to striking "through the ball" and nothing else. Try to imagine that the clubhead is going clean through the ball, and not that it has to be crushed.

I have found this conception of the of the blow to be the secret of straightness, provided always that the controlling power is performed by the left wrist. No doubt a longer ball, as I have proved for myself, can be driven by employing the right wrist, hand and forearm, but the degree of accuracy is much less than when directing the shot with the left."

Archie Compston, GOLF ILLUSTRATED, October 1925

MENS' OFFICIAL COURSE	**PAR**												
	DISTANCE												
	HANDICAP/STROKE INDEX												
A													
B													
	HOLE	**1**	**2**	**3**	**4**	**5**	**6**	**7**	**8**	**9**	**OUT**		
C													
D													
MATCHES													
LADIES' OFFICIAL COURSE	HANDICAP/STROKE INDEX												
	DISTANCE												
	PAR												

										REPAIR BALL MARKS	
10	**11**	**12**	**13**	**14**	**15**	**16**	**17**	**18**	**IN**	**TOTAL**	**HDCP**	**NET**
											REPLACE DIVOTS	

SCORER	ATTESTED	DATE

©

ROUND REPORT

Date: _____

Course: _____

Time started: _____ Time finished: _____

Weather: _____

Players: _____ Strokes received: _____

_____ _____

_____ _____

_____ _____

_____ _____

Competition details:

        Singles: _____   Greensome: _____

        Foursomes: _____   Stableford: _____

        3-ball: _____   Stroke-play: _____

        4-ball: _____   Match-play: _____

Stakes: _____

Best hole: _____

_____

Best shot: _____

_____

Incidents: _____

_____

_____

_____

Result: _____

_____

_____

_____

©

"The relation of the fairer part of creation to golf varies between that of a "golfer's widow" and that of a champion. Singleness of thought, concentration of purpose, quietude of manner, are essential in the game, and the expert golfer, whose tender mercies are ever cruel, will unhesitatingly cry "Fore" to the flutter of a golf cape or the tinkle of light feminine conversation. In the words of a promising young golfer, who found it hard to decide between flirtation and playing the game: "It's all very pleasant, but it isn't business". But the sincerity of their enthusiasm is so apparent, and their adaptability to the nicer points of the game so great that there are few clubs now where they are not firmly established, and where a man who has finished a hard day's play cannot take pleasure in an aftermath of tea and blandishments."

SCRIBNER'S MAGAZINE, May 1895

MENS' OFFICIAL COURSE	PAR										
	DISTANCE										
	HANDICAP / STROKE INDEX										
A											
B											
HOLE		1	2	3	4	5	6	7	8	9	OUT
C											
D											
MATCHES											
LADIES' OFFICIAL COURSE	HANDICAP / STROKE INDEX										
	DISTANCE										
	PAR										

									REPAIR BALL MARKS	
10	11	12	13	14	15	16	17	18	IN	TOTAL	HDCP	NET
											REPLACE DIVOTS	

| SCORER | ATTESTED | DATE |

ROUND REPORT

Date: _____

Course: _____

Time started: _____ Time finished: _____

Weather: _____

Players: _____ Strokes received: _____

_____   _____

_____   _____

_____   _____

_____   _____

Competition details:

Singles:	_____		Greensome:	_____	
Foursomes:	_____		Stableford:	_____	
3-ball:	_____		Stroke-play:	_____	
4-ball:	_____		Match-play:	_____	

Stakes: _____

Best hole: _____
_____

Best shot: _____
_____

Incidents: _____
_____
_____
_____

Result: _____
_____
_____
_____

©

"If you were assured that without imbibing any new-fangled religion and regardless of all the new dietists and doctors, you could not only add 20 years to the normal span of life, but secure in the present at least one good day out of seven by the simple process of swinging a golf club, would you not rush out to the nearest links and begin to take lessons?

It is to the many millions who have never even attempted to play that a few words of advice may be offered. If they will follow the advice given, we guarantee health, sleep, immunity from nervous prostration and business worries, good temper, mental control, and lastly long life – barring accidents from taxicabs or airships. If those long-lived people who discovered the virtues of the lactic acid had been nurtured on a golf links they would never have required germ tabloids to keep them alive."

OUTING, 1910

MENS' OFFICIAL COURSE	PAR											
	DISTANCE											
	HANDICAP/STROKE INDEX											
A												
B												
	HOLE	1	2	3	4	5	6	7	8	9	OUT
C												
D												
MATCHES												
LADIES' OFFICIAL COURSE	HANDICAP/STROKE INDEX											
	DISTANCE											
	PAR											

										REPAIR BALL MARKS	
10	11	12	13	14	15	16	17	18	IN	TOTAL	HDCP	NET
											REPLACE DIVOTS	

| SCORER | ATTESTED | DATE |

©

ROUND REPORT

Date: _____

Course: _____

Time started: _____ Time finished: _____

Weather: _____

Players: _____ Strokes received: _____

_____   _____

_____   _____

_____   _____

_____   _____

Competition details:

        Singles: _____   Greensome: _____

        Foursomes: _____   Stableford: _____

        3-ball: _____   Stroke-play: _____

        4-ball: _____   Match-play: _____

Stakes: _____

Best hole: _____

_____

Best shot: _____

_____

Incidents: _____

_____

_____

_____

Result: _____

_____

_____

_____

©

"Here is a tip for the golfer who plays once a week or maybe once in two weeks. A couple of days before going out to play, take a little time off and drive 50 or more balls into a driving net. Don't try to shoot a hole through the net; just simply hit every ball with a practice swing. The chances are, if he does this on Thursday, his hands will feel sore on Friday, and maybe still a bit sore on Saturday, but by Sunday they will feel fit and fine."

A real trouble with most of us is that we go out, say on Sunday morning, feeling fit and fine and expecting a good score – maybe we dreamed all about it the night before – but we get away to a ragged start, and by the time we have played four or five holes our hands begin to feel sore, and we are unable to hit a shot decently. The result is rotten golf, and pleasant anticipation is turned into bitter and disappointing reality.

THE AMERICAN GOLFER, June 1932

MENS' OFFICIAL COURSE	PAR										
	DISTANCE										
	HANDICAP/STROKE INDEX										
A											
B											
	HOLE	1	2	3	4	5	6	7	8	9	OUT
C											
D											
MATCHES											
LADIES' OFFICIAL COURSE	HANDICAP/STROKE INDEX										
	DISTANCE										
	PAR										

											REPAIR BALL MARKS
10	11	12	13	14	15	16	17	18	IN	TOTAL	HDCP	NET
											REPLACE DIVOTS

| SCORER | ATTESTED | DATE |

©

37

ROUND REPORT

Date: _____

Course: _____

Time started: _____ Time finished: _____

Weather: _____

Players: _____ Strokes received: _____

_____   _____

_____   _____

_____   _____

_____   _____

Competition details:

Singles: _____   Greensome: _____

Foursomes: _____   Stableford: _____

3-ball: _____   Stroke-play: _____

4-ball: _____   Match-play: _____

Stakes: _____

Best hole: _____

_____

Best shot: _____

_____

Incidents: _____

_____

_____

_____

Result: _____

_____

_____

_____

©

DURING A STRIKE OF CADDIES.

An amusing incident happened when the club was in Hagley Park. A strike of caddies occurred. The fee for a round was, I think, one shilling, and the caddies asked for one and a half. The club would not agree, and the caddies refused engagement. So far, so good: we would carry our own clubs.

However, when the next Saturday came round, all the caddies were congregated at the first tee. They still refused engagement, but, just as each player was going to drive off, they let out such a yell that is a wonder he did not miss the ball altogether; he certainly did not get a decent drive in. This went on until it could be borne no longer, and the caddies won."

THE CHRISTCHURCH SUN, NEW ZEALAND, October 1929

MENS' OFFICIAL COURSE	PAR										
	DISTANCE										
	HANDICAP/STROKE INDEX										
A											
B											
HOLE		**1**	**2**	**3**	**4**	**5**	**6**	**7**	**8**	**9**	**OUT**
C											
D											
MATCHES											
LADIES' OFFICIAL COURSE	HANDICAP/STROKE INDEX										
	DISTANCE										
	PAR										

										REPAIR BALL MARKS	
10	**11**	**12**	**13**	**14**	**15**	**16**	**17**	**18**	**IN**	**TOTAL**	**HDCP**	**NET**
										REPLACE DIVOTS	

SCORER	ATTESTED	DATE

©

ROUND REPORT

Date: _____

Course: _____

Time started: _____ Time finished: _____

Weather: _____

Players: _____ Strokes received: _____

_____ _____

_____ _____

_____ _____

_____ _____

Competition details:

Singles: _____ Greensome: _____

Foursomes: _____ Stableford: _____

3-ball: _____ Stroke-play: _____

4-ball: _____ Match-play: _____

Stakes: _____

Best hole: _____

_____

Best shot: _____

_____

Incidents: _____

_____

_____

_____

Result: _____

_____

_____

_____

©

"In addition to the recognized styles of famous golfers there are swings of diverse and wonderful grotesqueness – the "Pig-Tail" style, the bizarre "Headsman", the "Pendulum", the "Recoil", the "Hammerhurling", the "Double-jointed", the "Surprise", and the "Disappointment" – whose respective names are in a measure their explanation, the last-named not being applicable to the state of mind of the player, as one might suppose, but to that of the spectator, who finds that a faulty style in the beginning of a swing may often result in as clean a stroke as one could wish. These styles have all been characteristic of famous golfers, and with all of them the ball starts low-flying from the club, skims like a swallow's rise as the initial velocity begins to diminish, continues its career for 200 yards, and drops to the ground as gently as a bird alights."

SCRIBNER'S MAGAZINE, May 1895

MENS' OFFICIAL COURSE	PAR											
	DISTANCE											
	HANDICAP/STROKE INDEX											
A												
B												
HOLE		1	2	3	4	5	6	7	8	9	OUT
C												
D												
MATCHES												
LADIES' OFFICIAL COURSE	HANDICAP/STROKE INDEX											
	DISTANCE											
	PAR											

											REPAIR BALL MARKS	
10	11	12	13	14	15	16	17	18	IN	TOTAL	HDCP	NET
											REPLACE DIVOTS	
SCORER		ATTESTED			DATE			

©

ROUND REPORT

Date: _____

Course: _____

Time started: _____ Time finished: _____

Weather: _____

Players: _____ Strokes received: _____

_____ _____

_____ _____

_____ _____

_____ _____

Competition details:

Singles:	_____	Greensome:	_____
Foursomes:	_____	Stableford:	_____
3-ball:	_____	Stroke-play:	_____
4-ball:	_____	Match-play:	_____

Stakes: _____

Best hole: _____

_____

Best shot: _____

_____

Incidents: _____

_____

_____

_____

Result: _____

_____

_____

_____

©

"Watch the good players and see how slowly and easily they swing back. At first sight, you may think that they go back rather quickly, but that is only because the whole action is smooth and without apparent effort. But imitate them exactly as they stand in front of you and you will find that the backward motion is much slower than at first you imagine it to be. The backward swing should be just twice as slow as the forward movement to the ball. It isn't a bad plan to count "one – two" going back and "one" coming forward. By thus counting you compel yourself to go slowly.

Half the battle of golf consists in taking it easy. Irritation over a bad shot, anxiety over a bunker in front of you, and especially the effort to drive against a strong wind, may tempt you to hurry your swing. If you give in to the impulse, the result will be bad, and the habit will grow on you."

OUTING, 1910

MENS' OFFICIAL COURSE	PAR										
	DISTANCE										
	HANDICAP/STROKE INDEX										
A											
B											
	HOLE	1	2	3	4	5	6	7	8	9	OUT
C											
D											
MATCHES											
	HANDICAP/STROKE INDEX										
LADIES' OFFICIAL COURSE	DISTANCE										
	PAR										

										REPAIR BALL MARKS	
10	11	12	13	14	15	16	17	18	IN	TOTAL	HDCP	NET
											REPLACE DIVOTS	
SCORER			ATTESTED			DATE						

43

ROUND REPORT

Date: _____

Course: _____

Time started: _____ Time finished: _____

Weather: _____

Players: _____ Strokes received: _____

_____   _____

_____   _____

_____   _____

_____   _____

Competition details:

    Singles: _____   Greensome: _____

    Foursomes: _____   Stableford: _____

    3-ball: _____   Stroke-play: _____

    4-ball: _____   Match-play: _____

Stakes: _____

Best hole: _____

_____

Best shot: _____

_____

Incidents: _____

_____

_____

_____

Result: _____

_____

_____

_____

©

"To my mind, most golfers handle the matter of concentration in the wrong way. Many of them try to think of entirely too many things, with the result that they can, of course, concentrate on nothing. Others apparently think of nothing except trouble ahead, such as bunkers or ponds or out of bounds. While thinking of these, they can, of course, think of nothing in connection with the swing.

In my opinion, it is important for the average golfer to think of ease and comfort in the address. The next that he should centre on is a smooth, even backswing. The great mistake that most make is thinking ahead of the stroke, not with it. Never mind where the ball is going: first of all it has to be hit in the right way before it will go in the right place. Think of that side of the matter."

Glenna Collett Vane, THE AMERICAN GOLFER, June 1932

MENS' OFFICIAL COURSE	PAR										
	DISTANCE										
	HANDICAP/STROKE INDEX										
A											
B											
	HOLE	1	2	3	4	5	6	7	8	9	OUT
C											
D											
MATCHES											
LADIES' OFFICIAL COURSE	HANDICAP/STROKE INDEX										
	DISTANCE										
	PAR										

									REPAIR BALL MARKS	
10	11	12	13	14	15	16	17	18	IN	TOTAL	HDCP	NET
										REPLACE DIVOTS	

| SCORER | ATTESTED | DATE |

©

45

ROUND REPORT

Date:_____

Course:_____

Time started:_____ Time finished:_____

Weather:_____

Players: _____ Strokes received: _____

              _____   _____

              _____   _____

              _____   _____

              _____   _____

Competition details:

Singles:	_____	Greensome:	_____
Foursomes:	_____	Stableford:	_____
3-ball:	_____	Stroke-play:	_____
4-ball:	_____	Match-play:	_____

Stakes:_____

Best hole:_____

_____

Best shot:_____

_____

Incidents:_____

_____

_____

_____

Result:_____

_____

_____

_____

©

"**Golf for the Married: 1** We've all heard the tragedy of the golf widow – she sees to that. Hear Gladys broadcasting her sobstuff – "And I *never* see him – and when I *do* he talks of nothing but his horrid golf!" **2** Far different is George's wife, who encourages him all she can – with helpful hints. As he drives wild through the clubhouse window she brightly chirps – "Don't you think if you hit it a *little* more gently, dear". George, who realizes what a true helpmate his little woman is, manfully refrains from braining her with a niblick. **3** Harriett, so her husband thinks, should be a *proud* wife. Back in 1920, Albert made *a hole in one*. To date, Harriet has heard the details 2,587 times. The brave girl can still smile."

WHAT CHEER! SACRAMENTO, April 1927

MENS' OFFICIAL COURSE	PAR											
	DISTANCE											
	HANDICAP/STROKE INDEX											
A												
B												
	HOLE	**1**	**2**	**3**	**4**	**5**	**6**	**7**	**8**	**9**	**OUT**
C												
D												
MATCHES												
LADIES' OFFICIAL COURSE	HANDICAP/STROKE INDEX											
	DISTANCE											
	PAR											

									REPAIR BALL MARKS	
10	**11**	**12**	**13**	**14**	**15**	**16**	**17**	**18**	**IN**	**TOTAL**	**HDCP**	**NET**
											REPLACE DIVOTS	
SCORER		**ATTESTED**			**DATE**					

47

ROUND REPORT

Date:_____

Course:_____

Time started:_____ Time finished:_____

Weather:_____

Players: _____ Strokes received: _____

_____ _____

_____ _____

_____ _____

_____ _____

Competition details:

Singles: _____   Greensome: _____

Foursomes: _____   Stableford: _____

3-ball: _____   Stroke-play: _____

4-ball: _____   Match-play: _____

Stakes:_____

Best hole:_____

_____

Best shot:_____

_____

Incidents:_____

_____

_____

_____

Result:_____

_____

_____

_____

"The game can be played in company or alone. Robinson Crusoe on his island, with his man Friday as a caddie, could have realized the golfer's dream of perfect happiness – a fine day, a good course, and a clear green. If Henry VIII had cultivated the more delicate emotions by taking to the links of the Knuckle Club, he might have saved his body from the gout and his name from the contempt of posterity; he might have dismissed the sittings of the Divorce Court and gone to play a foursome with Cromwell, Wolsey, and the Papal Legate; and all the abbey lands which fell to the nobles would have been converted into golfing greens by the fiat of the royal golfer."

SCRIBNER'S MAGAZINE, May 1895

MENS' OFFICIAL COURSE	PAR										
	DISTANCE										
	HANDICAP/STROKE INDEX										
A											
B											
	HOLE	1	2	3	4	5	6	7	8	9	OUT
C											
D											
MATCHES											
LADIES' OFFICIAL COURSE	HANDICAP/STROKE INDEX										
	DISTANCE										
	PAR										

										REPAIR BALL MARKS	
10	11	12	13	14	15	16	17	18	IN	TOTAL	HDCP	NET
										REPLACE DIVOTS	

SCORER   ATTESTED   DATE

©

ROUND REPORT

Date:_____

Course:_____

Time started:_____ Time finished:_____

Weather:_____

Players: _____ Strokes received: _____

_____   _____

_____   _____

_____   _____

_____   _____

Competition details:

Singles:	_____	Greensome:	_____
Foursomes:	_____	Stableford:	_____
3-ball:	_____	Stroke-play:	_____
4-ball:	_____	Match-play:	_____

Stakes:_____

Best hole:_____

_____

Best shot:_____

_____

Incidents:_____

_____

_____

_____

Result :_____

_____

_____

_____

©

"The few really good putters are, curiously enough, generally weak in their play through the green or in their driving, and one rarely meets a player who is proficient in all three. "Putting is an Inspiration," we are told, but I am more incline to agree with the man who so sapiently said, "Putting is the Devil!". On days when every putt goes down, no matter how remote you may be from the hole, you are ready to say proudly, "Putting is an Inspiration," but on other days, when you are losing hole after hole through atrocious putting, you would fain proclaim aloud the other sentiment. Practising putting on a lawn is very little assistance, except in improving the aim. Every putting green is (or ought to be) different from the last."

BADMINTON MAGAZINE, 1898

MENS' OFFICIAL COURSE	PAR										
	DISTANCE										
	HANDICAP / STROKE INDEX										
A											
B											
	HOLE	1	2	3	4	5	6	7	8	9	OUT
C											
D											
MATCHES											
LADIES' OFFICIAL COURSE	HANDICAP / STROKE INDEX										
	DISTANCE										
	PAR										

10	11	12	13	14	15	16	17	18	IN	TOTAL	HDCP	NET	REPAIR BALL MARKS
													REPLACE DIVOTS

SCORER	ATTESTED	DATE

ROUND REPORT

Date: _____

Course: _____

Time started: _____ Time finished: _____

Weather: _____

Players: _____ Strokes received: _____

        _____   _____

        _____   _____

        _____   _____

        _____   _____

Competition details:

Singles:	_____	Greensome:	_____
Foursomes:	_____	Stableford:	_____
3-ball:	_____	Stroke-play:	_____
4-ball:	_____	Match-play:	_____

Stakes: _____

Best hole: _____
_____

Best shot: _____
_____

Incidents: _____
_____
_____
_____

Result: _____
_____
_____
_____

©

"The true golfer is critical of lucky strokes or flukes; in his estimation they are as discreditable as bad ones; certainty and precision is his standard, and his comment in broad Scotch, the real golf language, after a bad shot by a good player, calculated to draw applause from more ignorant bystanders, would probably be: "My, but you was a lucky yin, bad play – didna desairve it".

George Glennie, a famous player whose purism was proverbial, once in a foursome drove his ball into a burn; his partner, wading in with boots and stockings, took the ball on the wing with his niblick as it floated down, and laid it dead at the hole. "Well, what about that stroke?" said his partner to the sage, who had preserved an unyielding silence. "No golf at a'" – then, in a soliloquy, "just monkey's tricks"."

SCRIBNER'S MAGAZINE, May 1895

MENS' OFFICIAL COURSE	PAR												
	DISTANCE												
	HANDICAP / STROKE INDEX												
A													
B													
	HOLE	1	2	3	4	5	6	7	8	9	OUT		
C													
D													
MATCHES													
LADIES' OFFICIAL COURSE	HANDICAP / STROKE INDEX												
	DISTANCE												
	PAR												

										REPAIR BALL MARKS	
10	11	12	13	14	15	16	17	18	IN	TOTAL	HDCP	NET
									REPLACE DIVOTS	

| SCORER | ATTESTED | DATE |

ROUND REPORT

Date:_____

Course:_____

Time started:_____ Time finished:_____

Weather:_____

Players: _____ Strokes received: _____

              _____   _____

              _____   _____

              _____   _____

              _____   _____

Competition details:

Singles:	_____	Greensome:	_____
Foursomes:	_____	Stableford:	_____
3-ball:	_____	Stroke-play:	_____
4-ball:	_____	Match-play:	_____

Stakes:_____

Best hole:_____

_____

Best shot:_____

_____

Incidents:_____

_____

_____

_____

Result:_____

_____

_____

_____

©

"A movement of the gallery had shut off my view, but I couldn't have looked anyway. And I could tell with a deadly certainty what was happening   The breathing ceased. He was addressing the ball   A thin click, and the beginning of a kind of sigh – the ball was on its way. The sigh grew louder ... it changed to a gasp .... Missed!

No!

The gasp changed to a roar, the stunning crash of a thunderbolt that strikes at your feet.

The ball had rolled, slowly and more slowly, to the rim of the hole; hesitated – stopped. And then ...

Well, then it had dropped."

The 1929 US Open, by OB Keeler, A BOY'S LIFE OF BOBBY JONES, 1931

MENS' OFFICIAL COURSE	PAR										
	DISTANCE										
	HANDICAP/STROKE INDEX										
A											
B											
	HOLE	1	2	3	4	5	6	7	8	9	OUT
C											
D											
MATCHES											
LADIES' OFFICIAL COURSE	HANDICAP/STROKE INDEX										
	DISTANCE										
	PAR										

										REPAIR BALL MARKS	
10	11	12	13	14	15	16	17	18	IN	TOTAL	HDCP	NET
											REPLACE DIVOTS	
SCORER		ATTESTED			DATE							

©

ROUND REPORT

Date: _____

Course: _____

Time started: _____ Time finished: _____

Weather: _____

Players: _____ Strokes received: _____

_____ _____

_____ _____

_____ _____

_____ _____

Competition details:

Singles: _____ Greensome: _____

Foursomes: _____ Stableford: _____

3-ball: _____ Stroke-play: _____

4-ball: _____ Match-play: _____

Stakes: _____

Best hole: _____

_____

Best shot: _____

_____

Incidents: _____

_____

_____

_____

Result: _____

_____

_____

_____

©

"It is one of the traditions of the great players at St Andrews, that it was their guiding principle never to make a bad shot. An easy theory to enunciate, but the great army of amateurs who with heart-breaking efforts have striven to rise to that standard, and the record of their topped balls, broken clubs, misses and foozles at critical stages in a match, can bear witness to the difficulty of reducing it satisfactorily to practice. The merit of these fine golfers was that their play was sure – as they played today, so they would play tomorrow; there was nothing unequal in them, no wavering, no unexpected breakdown at a moment when the championship might depend on a single stroke. They have been known to play 90 consecutive holes without one bad shot or one stroke made otherwise than as was intended."

SCRIBNER'S MAGAZINE, May 1895

MENS' OFFICIAL COURSE	PAR										
	DISTANCE										
	HANDICAP/STROKE INDEX										
A											
B											
	HOLE	1	2	3	4	5	6	7	8	9	OUT
C											
D											
MATCHES											
LADIES' OFFICIAL COURSE	HANDICAP/STROKE INDEX										
	DISTANCE										
	PAR										

									REPAIR BALL MARKS	
10	11	12	13	14	15	16	17	18	IN	TOTAL	HDCP	NET
									REPLACE DIVOTS	
SCORER		ATTESTED			DATE					

57

ROUND REPORT

Date: _____

Course: _____

Time started: _____ Time finished: _____

Weather: _____

Players: _____ Strokes received: _____

_____ _____

_____ _____

_____ _____

_____ _____

Competition details:

Singles:	_____	Greensome:	_____
Foursomes:	_____	Stableford:	_____
3-ball:	_____	Stroke-play:	_____
4-ball:	_____	Match-play:	_____

Stakes: _____

Best hole: _____

_____

Best shot: _____

_____

Incidents: _____

_____

_____

_____

Result: _____

_____

_____

_____

©

"Indeed, it is not too much to say that the American caddie is the worst in the world; every golfer knows what it is to have his day at the game literally poisoned by the laziness, the ignorance and the insolence of the average club carrier. But let us be fair to the boys, for it is entirely our own fault. For example, in Great Britain, a player never touches his ball from the beginning to the end of the round. The caddie tees it (and tees it properly); picks it out of the cup, cleans it and indeed does everything but hit it. When golf began in this country our players were too impatient to train the caddies in their appropriate duties; the golfer wanted to do everything himself, and he never dreamed of enlisting the active interest of the boy in his play. The caddie was treated as a beast of burden, and such he remains today, an expensive and intolerable nuisance."

THE YEAR IN GOLF, 1906

MENS' OFFICIAL COURSE	PAR										
	DISTANCE										
	HANDICAP/STROKE INDEX										
A											
B											
	HOLE	1	2	3	4	5	6	7	8	9	OUT
C											
D											
MATCHES											
LADIES' OFFICIAL COURSE	HANDICAP/STROKE INDEX										
	DISTANCE										
	PAR										

										REPAIR BALL MARKS	
10	11	12	13	14	15	16	17	18	IN	TOTAL	HDCP	NET
											REPLACE DIVOTS	

SCORER   ATTESTED   DATE

ROUND REPORT

Date:_____

Course:_____

Time started:_____ Time finished:_____

Weather:_____

Players: _____   Strokes received: _____

_____   _____

_____   _____

_____   _____

_____   _____

Competition details:

Singles: _____   Greensome: _____

Foursomes: _____   Stableford: _____

3-ball: _____   Stroke-play: _____

4-ball: _____   Match-play: _____

Stakes:_____

Best hole:_____

_____

Best shot:_____

_____

Incidents:_____

_____

_____

_____

Result:_____

_____

_____

_____

©

"The drive, however, as many insist, is but the prelude, and, therefore, the least important of the shots. It passes many a pitfall, reduces the dangers that lurk in cuppy lies, bastion bunkers, pit bunkers and hazards, but the approach shots in playing "through the green" are the true test of skill, nerve and temper, and cut a greater figure in the score than the drive from the teeing-ground. The term "approach shot", in its common acceptation, conveys the idea of a stroke played with the iron with something less than the full swing, and involves differences in distance, elevation and style. Then comes in the nice judgement as to three-quarter shots, half-shots, and wrist shots to cover the distance, the straight forward stroke, or the cut in making any of these ...... To see a finished artist at this work is a sight that lingers long in the memory .... "

SCRIBNER'S MAGAZINE, May 1895

MENS' OFFICIAL COURSE	PAR										
	DISTANCE										
	HANDICAP/STROKE INDEX										
A											
B											
	HOLE	1	2	3	4	5	6	7	8	9	OUT
C											
D											
MATCHES											
	HANDICAP/STROKE INDEX										
LADIES' OFFICIAL COURSE	DISTANCE										
	PAR										

										REPAIR BALL MARKS	
10	11	12	13	14	15	16	17	18	IN	TOTAL	HDCP	NET
											REPLACE DIVOTS	

| SCORER | ATTESTED | DATE |

ROUND REPORT

Date: _____

Course: _____

Time started: _____ Time finished: _____

Weather: _____

Players: _____ Strokes received: _____

_____   _____

_____   _____

_____   _____

_____   _____

Competition details:

      Singles: _____   Greensome: _____

      Foursomes: _____   Stableford: _____

      3-ball: _____   Stroke-play: _____

      4-ball: _____   Match-play: _____

Stakes: _____

Best hole: _____

_____

Best shot: _____

_____

Incidents: _____

_____

_____

_____

Result: _____

_____

_____

_____

©

"I have tried wooden putters, gunmetal putters, straight-faced putters, cylindrical putters, mallet-headed putters, putting cleeks, cleeks, left-handed putting cleeks – in short, the whole family of every conceivable kind of weapon that human ingenuity has evolved for the purpose. I have tried them all in every imaginable position – off the left leg, standing square, off the right leg, facing the hole; have had them equipped with long and short shafts with straight faces, with varying degrees of loft, and, antithetically, with the face turned in – and, at times, have putted extraordinarily well with each and every member of the tribe.

The sum of it all is, that my experience shows conclusively that the really good putter is largely born, not made, and is endowed with a good eye and a tactile delicacy of grip which are denied the ordinary run of mortals."

OUTING, July 1900

MENS' OFFICIAL COURSE	PAR										
	DISTANCE										
	HANDICAP/STROKE INDEX										
A											
B											
	HOLE	**1**	**2**	**3**	**4**	**5**	**6**	**7**	**8**	**9**	**OUT**
C											
D											
MATCHES											
LADIES' OFFICIAL COURSE	HANDICAP/STROKE INDEX										
	DISTANCE										
	PAR										

										REPAIR BALL MARKS	
10	**11**	**12**	**13**	**14**	**15**	**16**	**17**	**18**	**IN**	**TOTAL**	**HDCP**	**NET**
										REPLACE DIVOTS	
SCORER		ATTESTED			DATE						

©

ROUND REPORT

Date: _____

Course: _____

Time started: _____ Time finished: _____

Weather: _____

Players: _____ Strokes received: _____

    _____   _____

    _____   _____

    _____   _____

    _____   _____

Competition details:

Singles:	_____	Greensome:	_____
Foursomes:	_____	Stableford:	_____
3-ball:	_____	Stroke-play:	_____
4-ball:	_____	Match-play:	_____

Stakes: _____

Best hole: _____

_____

Best shot: _____

_____

Incidents: _____

_____

_____

_____

Result: _____

_____

_____

_____

©

"On the links the other day, two men were having a hot game. Just as one of them stepped up to the tee for the sixth, a very swagger cart came spinning up. A stunning young woman was driving … She called: "George, dear, won't you come home now and not delay luncheon?". The man straightened with an air of disgust: "Not now, I'm playing the game of my life. I'm breaking my record by 10 strokes." "Well, I'll wait," she said.

"George dear" continued the game of his life. He sliced his drive and lost his ball in the blackberry bushes in the ravine. He teed a new ball and lost one stroke. Then he topped into the whins, and, playing his niblick, didn't gain three feet. He lost two strokes and the rest of his temper.

Ten minutes later, the young woman was driving the cart. In the back, heels dangling, was "George, dear". The game of his life was over."

THE AMERICAN CRICKETER, May 1912

MENS' OFFICIAL COURSE	PAR											
	DISTANCE											
	HANDICAP / STROKE INDEX											
A												
B												
HOLE		1	2	3	4	5	6	7	8	9	OUT	
C												
D												
MATCHES												
LADIES' OFFICIAL COURSE	HANDICAP / STROKE INDEX											
	DISTANCE											
	PAR											

									REPAIR BALL MARKS		
10	11	12	13	14	15	16	17	18	IN	TOTAL	HDCP	NET
										REPLACE DIVOTS		
SCORER		ATTESTED			DATE							

©

ROUND REPORT

Date: _____

Course: _____

Time started: _____ Time finished: _____

Weather: _____

Players: _____ Strokes received: _____

_____ _____

_____ _____

_____ _____

_____ _____

Competition details:

          Singles: _____   Greensome: _____

          Foursomes: _____   Stableford: _____

          3-ball: _____   Stroke-play: _____

          4-ball: _____   Match-play: _____

Stakes: _____

Best hole: _____

_____

Best shot: _____

_____

Incidents: _____

_____

_____

_____

Result: _____

_____

_____

_____

©

"To the novice, it seems the simplest of sports, but to the expert the most complicated; to him it is a "thing of beauty and a joy forever". The scoffer who speaks with a contempt not born of familiarity, or views it with assumed indifference, may assert that the game, with its system of strokes and score, will restore the unhealthy atmosphere of the croquet ground; that it will try the souls of the clergy and become the undoing of parishioners.

He may watch with a pitying and ill-disguised contempt the frantic efforts of stout elderly gentlemen to extricate a ball from a hazard, and say, as an old farmer did, who leaned over the fence and smiled placidly at a perspiring banker: "Don't you think you're pretty big for that little marble?" – yet he cannot stay its triumphant progress."

SCRIBNER'S MAGAZINE, May 1895

MENS' OFFICIAL COURSE	PAR										
	DISTANCE										
	HANDICAP/STROKE INDEX										
A											
B											
	HOLE	1	2	3	4	5	6	7	8	9	OUT
C											
D											
MATCHES											
LADIES' OFFICIAL COURSE	HANDICAP/STROKE INDEX										
	DISTANCE										
	PAR										

										REPAIR BALL MARKS	
10	11	12	13	14	15	16	17	18	IN	TOTAL	HDCP	NET
											REPLACE DIVOTS	

| SCORER | ATTESTED | DATE |

©

ROUND REPORT

Date:_____

Course:_____

Time started:_____ Time finished:_____

Weather:_____

Players: _____ Strokes received: _____

      _____   _____

      _____   _____

      _____   _____

      _____   _____

Competition details:

Singles:	_____	Greensome:	_____
Foursomes:	_____	Stableford:	_____
3-ball:	_____	Stroke-play:	_____
4-ball:	_____	Match-play:	_____

Stakes:_____

Best hole:_____

_____

Best shot:_____

_____

Incidents:_____

_____

_____

_____

Result :_____

_____

_____

_____

©

"The learning of golf is a slow and tedious business at the best; though illumined by many flashes of hope, the clouds of despair darken it in equal number. The exasperating thing is that the secret seems always to be escaping you; for a day, perhaps for a week, you may surprise and delight yourself by playing your iron to the general admiration. You think you have acquired the stroke of beauty as a joy for ever: the next day it may have utterly gone from you. The consolation is that it will return. At a certain, stage of your education you will find yourself playing your iron well one day, your driver well the third. "Oh!" you keep on explaining, "if only I could catch a day on which I could play all three!" But that glad day does not hasten to arrive: you will know the sickness of hope deferred again and again before it comes to you; and when at length it comes, it passes."

OUTING, November 1896

MENS' OFFICIAL COURSE	PAR										
	DISTANCE										
	HANDICAP/STROKE INDEX										
A											
B											
	HOLE	1	2	3	4	5	6	7	8	9	OUT
C											
D											
MATCHES											
LADIES' OFFICIAL COURSE	HANDICAP/STROKE INDEX										
	DISTANCE										
	PAR										

										REPAIR BALL MARKS	
10	11	12	13	14	15	16	17	18	IN	TOTAL	HDCP	NET
										REPLACE DIVOTS	
SCORER			ATTESTED				DATE				

69

ROUND REPORT

Date:_____

Course:_____

Time started:_____ Time finished:_____

Weather:_____

Players: _____ Strokes received: _____

           _____   _____

           _____   _____

           _____   _____

           _____   _____

Competition details:

        Singles: _____   Greensome: _____

        Foursomes: _____   Stableford: _____

        3-ball: _____   Stroke-play:_____

        4-ball: _____   Match-play:_____

Stakes:_____

Best hole:_____

_____

Best shot:_____

_____

Incidents:_____

_____

_____

_____

Result:_____

_____

_____

_____

©

"First there is the matter of divots. For some reason, this seems to be one of the chief hobbies of the Committee. Everywhere we go, everything we read, all we hear and see is "REPLACE DIVOTS". But how, I ask you, can one pick up a few stray blades of grass, put them in a 10-inch hole, stamp heavily on them and expect them to grow? Here's the answer.

With the large bags we are carrying these days, there is ample room for one or two more sticks. Therefore it's no trick to grab the rake and hoe from the cellar before leaving home and drop them in the golf bag. Then while the caddie is wandering around playing at looking for your ball, a few strokes with the rake, a little furrowing with the hoe, one or two daft gestures with the hands, and presto – the job is done. Think of it: no more worries about being imprisoned for not replacing divots."

PUTT, PUTT, PUTT, September 1928

MENS' OFFICIAL COURSE	PAR											
	DISTANCE											
	HANDICAP/STROKE INDEX											
A												
B												
HOLE		**1**	**2**	**3**	**4**	**5**	**6**	**7**	**8**	**9**	**OUT**
C												
D												
MATCHES												
LADIES' OFFICIAL COURSE	HANDICAP/STROKE INDEX											
	DISTANCE											
	PAR											

										REPAIR BALL MARKS	
10	**11**	**12**	**13**	**14**	**15**	**16**	**17**	**18**	**IN**	**TOTAL**	**HDCP**	**NET**
											REPLACE DIVOTS	

SCORER	ATTESTED	DATE

ROUND REPORT

Date:_____

Course:_____

Time started:_____ Time finished:_____

Weather:_____

Players: _____ Strokes received: _____

_____   _____

_____   _____

_____   _____

_____   _____

Competition details:

Singles: _____   Greensome: _____

Foursomes: _____   Stableford: _____

3-ball: _____   Stroke-play: _____

4-ball: _____   Match-play: _____

Stakes:_____

Best hole:_____

_____

Best shot:_____

_____

Incidents:_____

_____

_____

_____

Result:_____

_____

_____

_____

©

"From the moment one of the Philistines essays a stroke, and by accident makes a fair drive from a tee, his conversion is assured, he has gone through all the phases, and learned "to endure, then pity, then embrace"; the game then becomes dangerously near being interesting; henceforth he will strive persistently, in season and out of season, to show "the golf that is in him"; he will regret the neglected opportunities of his youth, and the disease which has no microbe and no cure is chronic and seated on him for life. Henceforward, he will adapt the motto of the Hittormissit Club: "Drive it if you can, club it if you will, kick it if you must.""

SCRIBNER'S MAGAZINE, May 1895

MENS' OFFICIAL COURSE	PAR											
	DISTANCE											
	HANDICAP/STROKE INDEX											
A												
B												
	HOLE	1	2	3	4	5	6	7	8	9	OUT	
C												
D												
MATCHES												
LADIES' OFFICIAL COURSE	HANDICAP/STROKE INDEX											
	DISTANCE											
	PAR											

										REPAIR BALL MARKS	
10	11	12	13	14	15	16	17	18	IN	TOTAL	HDCP	NET
											REPLACE DIVOTS	
SCORER			ATTESTED			DATE					

ROUND REPORT

Date:_____

Course:_____

Time started:_____ Time finished:_____

Weather:_____

Players: _____ Strokes received: _____

       _____   _____

       _____   _____

       _____   _____

       _____   _____

Competition details:

Singles:	_____		Greensome:	_____
Foursomes:	_____		Stableford:	_____
3-ball:	_____		Stroke-play:	_____
4-ball:	_____		Match-play:	_____

Stakes:_____

Best hole:_____

_____

Best shot:_____

_____

Incidents:_____

_____

_____

_____

Result:_____

_____

_____

_____

©

"A famous London physician told a *Morning Post* writer that "The process of growing old is best checked by my favourite prescription – golf *quant. suff.*"

"The retired business man often goes to pieces very quickly owing to a lack of customary application; well, golf gives him a pre-occupation that adds a new zest to life and prevents him from brooding over the burden of years. He tries to get round in 90, and, though he does not succeed, he lives to be 90 years old."

The correspondent adds that he was told the other day of a Scottish farmer, aged 78, who took part in a club match and went round an exacting course in 76, which must be almost a record. When asked how he contrived to keep so young, he replied: "By medicinal doses of golf"."

THE EDINBURGH UNIVERSITY GAMBOLIER, October 1922

MENS' OFFICIAL COURSE	PAR										
	DISTANCE										
	HANDICAP/STROKE INDEX										
A											
B											
	HOLE	1	2	3	4	5	6	7	8	9	OUT
C											
D											
MATCHES											
LADIES' OFFICIAL COURSE	HANDICAP/STROKE INDEX										
	DISTANCE										
	PAR										

											REPAIR BALL MARKS
10	11	12	13	14	15	16	17	18	IN	TOTAL	HDCP	NET
											REPLACE DIVOTS	
SCORER			ATTESTED				DATE					

ROUND REPORT

Date:_____

Course:_____

Time started:_____ Time finished:_____

Weather:_____

Players: _____ Strokes received: _____

        _____ _____

        _____ _____

        _____ _____

        _____ _____

Competition details:

Singles:	_____	Greensome:	_____
Foursomes:	_____	Stableford:	_____
3-ball:	_____	Stroke-play:	_____
4-ball:	_____	Match-play:	_____

Stakes:_____

Best hole:_____

_____

Best shot:_____

_____

Incidents:_____

_____

_____

_____

Result:_____

_____

_____

_____

©

"There is one person you cannot deceive in this world, and that is your caddie. He knows all your shortcomings, both of skill and character, and he is not slow to let you find them out. No golfer is a hero to his own caddie. The Scotch caddie had, and still has, the most supreme contempt for the golfer who goes round the links with scorecard and pencil. Old Crawford's saying is immortal.

"D'ye see that fellow?" he said in a loud tone of voice, indicating an Englishman who was laboriously adding up his score on a neighbouring putting green; "D'ye ken the best club in his set?" – then, with great contempt, "It's his pencil."

OUTING, 1910

MENS' OFFICIAL COURSE	PAR										
	DISTANCE										
	HANDICAP/STROKE INDEX										
A											
B											
	HOLE	1	2	3	4	5	6	7	8	9	OUT
C											
D											
MATCHES											
LADIES' OFFICIAL COURSE	HANDICAP/STROKE INDEX										
	DISTANCE										
	PAR										

									REPAIR BALL MARKS	
10	11	12	13	14	15	16	17	18	IN	TOTAL	HDCP	NET
										REPLACE DIVOTS	
SCORER		ATTESTED		DATE								

ROUND REPORT

Date: _____

Course: _____

Time started: _____ Time finished: _____

Weather: _____

Players: _____ Strokes received: _____

     _____   _____

     _____   _____

     _____   _____

     _____   _____

Competition details:

Singles:	_____	Greensome:	_____
Foursomes:	_____	Stableford:	_____
3-ball:	_____	Stroke-play:	_____
4-ball:	_____	Match-play:	_____

Stakes: _____

Best hole: _____

_____

Best shot: _____

_____

Incidents: _____

_____

_____

_____

Result: _____

_____

_____

_____

©

"**Definitions: Golf** – A two-and-a-half mile hike cross-country with a five-pound load, in the attempt to knock a small ball into 18 consecutive holes by 18 faultlessly executed shots. Generally attended by failure.

Tennis – A struggle between two players, each equally intent on making the opponent drop dead through running to retrieve a bouncing ball 40 feet to one side of him with no other instrument than a wooden frame enclosing the insides of a cat.

Wrestling – The application of scientific principles of weight, leverage and momentum to human relationships, culminating in the successful effort of one mass of beef to induce another to assume an uncomfortable horizontal position, with the alternative of getting his neck broken.

Baseball – A game of chance."

LIFE MAGAZINE, April 1927

MENS' OFFICIAL COURSE	PAR												
	DISTANCE												
	HANDICAP/STROKE INDEX												
A													
B													
	HOLE	1	2	3	4	5	6	7	8	9	OUT		
C													
D													
MATCHES													
LADIES' OFFICIAL COURSE	HANDICAP/STROKE INDEX												
	DISTANCE												
	PAR												

										REPAIR BALL MARKS	
10	11	12	13	14	15	16	17	18	IN	TOTAL	HDCP	NET
										REPLACE DIVOTS	
SCORER			ATTESTED				DATE				

ROUND REPORT

Date: _____

Course: _____

Time started: _____ Time finished: _____

Weather: _____

Players: _____ Strokes received: _____

_____ _____

_____ _____

_____ _____

_____ _____

Competition details:

        Singles: _____   Greensome: _____

        Foursomes: _____   Stableford: _____

        3-ball: _____   Stroke-play: _____

        4-ball: _____   Match-play: _____

Stakes: _____

Best hole: _____

_____

Best shot: _____

_____

Incidents: _____

_____

_____

_____

Result: _____

_____

_____

_____

©

"The loose, slashing style known as the St Andrew's swing, in which the player seems to twist his body into an imitation of the Laocoon, and then suddenly to uncoil, is the perfection of art. It is a swing and not a hit; the ball is met at a certain point and swept away with apparent abandon, the driver following the ball, and finishing with a swing over the shoulder in what is almost a complete circle.

A jerk is an abomination; the true motion requires a gradual acceleration of speed, with muscles flexible, save that the lower hand should have a tight grip on the stick – a swing like "an auld wife cutting hay"; if this does not convey the idea, "Eh man, just take and throw your club at the ba'." Oh! the careless ease of that swing and the beautiful far-reaching results that follow."

SCRIBNER'S MAGAZINE, May 1895

MENS' OFFICIAL COURSE	PAR										
	DISTANCE										
	HANDICAP / STROKE INDEX										
A											
B											
	HOLE	1	2	3	4	5	6	7	8	9	OUT
C											
D											
MATCHES											
LADIES' OFFICIAL COURSE	HANDICAP / STROKE INDEX										
	DISTANCE										
	PAR										

										REPAIR BALL MARKS	
10	11	12	13	14	15	16	17	18	IN	TOTAL	HDCP	NET
										REPLACE DIVOTS	
SCORER		ATTESTED			DATE							

©

ROUND REPORT

Date: _____

Course: _____

Time started: _____ Time finished: _____

Weather: _____

Players: _____ Strokes received: _____

_____ _____

_____ _____

_____ _____

_____ _____

Competition details:

Singles: _____ Greensome: _____

Foursomes: _____ Stableford: _____

3-ball: _____ Stroke-play: _____

4-ball: _____ Match-play: _____

Stakes: _____

Best hole: _____

_____

Best shot: _____

_____

Incidents: _____

_____

_____

_____

Result: _____

_____

_____

_____

©

"The golfer is essentially a hero-worshipper; and not only is he a hero-worshipper, but he has faith in the methods of heroes, a faith that is touching. He has at the same time a sublime confidence, although hitherto latent, in his own abilities for heroic achievement; he has not a doubt that, by adopting the methods of his heroes, he will join the demigods on Olympian heights. Which means, put into language more suited to the comprehension of the golfer, that every golfer has an inextinguishable faith that if he has his clubs made on the pattern of Harry Vardon, and can get just his crook of the elbow and overlapping grip, he will be just as fine a player. Why should he not?"

Horace Hutchinson, 1900

MENS' OFFICIAL COURSE	PAR											
	DISTANCE											
	HANDICAP / STROKE INDEX											
A												
B												
	HOLE	1	2	3	4	5	6	7	8	9	OUT
C												
D												
MATCHES												
LADIES' OFFICIAL COURSE	HANDICAP / STROKE INDEX											
	DISTANCE											
	PAR											

									REPAIR BALL MARKS		
10	11	12	13	14	15	16	17	18	IN	TOTAL	HDCP	NET
										REPLACE DIVOTS		

SCORER   ATTESTED   DATE

83

ROUND REPORT

Date:_____

Course:_____

Time started:_____ Time finished:_____

Weather:_____

Players:_____ Strokes received:_____

        _____   _____

        _____   _____

        _____   _____

        _____

Competition details:

Singles:	_____		Greensome:	_____
Foursomes:	_____		Stableford:	_____
3-ball:	_____		Stroke-play:	_____
4-ball:	_____		Match-play:	_____

Stakes:_____

Best hole:_____

_____

Best shot:_____

_____

Incidents:_____

_____

_____

_____

Result:_____

_____

_____

_____

©

"There is no royal road to the hole. Some men play well in the most awkward and contorted positions – positions which seem to invite a lack of success. Their success, however, proves that by whatever means the result is brought about, one thing is clear – the face of the club must have met the ball squarely at the crucial moment of sending it on its errand – which is the essence of good putting.

That's about all there is in it: to strike the ball truly in the centre, and with the necessary strength. There is no mystery about it. If the ball is struck exactly at the central point in line with the hole, by the middle of the club, with the face of it at right angles to the line to the hole, and kept so for an inch or so after the moment of impact, it is bound to go straight."

OUTING, July 1900

MENS' OFFICIAL COURSE	PAR											
	DISTANCE											
	HANDICAP/STROKE INDEX											
A												
B												
	HOLE	1	2	3	4	5	6	7	8	9	OUT
C												
D												
MATCHES												
LADIES' OFFICIAL COURSE	HANDICAP/STROKE INDEX											
	DISTANCE											
	PAR											

										REPAIR BALL MARKS	
10	11	12	13	14	15	16	17	18	IN	TOTAL	HDCP	NET
											REPLACE DIVOTS	
SCORER		ATTESTED			DATE							

©

ROUND REPORT

Date: _____

Course: _____

Time started: _____ Time finished: _____

Weather: _____

Players: _____ Strokes received: _____

      _____   _____

      _____   _____

      _____   _____

      _____   _____

Competition details:

Singles:	_____	Greensome:	_____
Foursomes:	_____	Stableford:	_____
3-ball:	_____	Stroke-play:	_____
4-ball:	_____	Match-play:	_____

Stakes: _____

Best hole: _____

_____

Best shot: _____

_____

Incidents: _____

_____

_____

_____

Result: _____

_____

_____

_____

©

"Once, long ago, to my shame but to my profit, I played a man of nine handicap, or thereabout, with a putter in the morning and a niblick in the afternoon. The putter was all very well – after all, what is a wooden putter but a driver in little, and what an iron putter but a slightly modified cleek? – but the niblick really made the game hard work with a solid "gutty" ball.

But, on the whole, what surprises both the good player as well as the bad – but the former far less, though far more pleasantly than the latter – is the high quality of the game, or, at all events, in the low scores for the holes, that can be achieved with one club only, no matter what that club be. When we find ourselves going round with a single club in very much the same score as when we have the full paraphernalia, we are almost inclined to wonder whether this simple golfing life is not the ideal thing."

GOLF MONTHLY, March 1912

MENS' OFFICIAL COURSE	PAR										
	DISTANCE										
	HANDICAP/STROKE INDEX										
A											
B											
	HOLE	1	2	3	4	5	6	7	8	9	OUT
C											
D											
MATCHES											
LADIES' OFFICIAL COURSE	HANDICAP/STROKE INDEX										
	DISTANCE										
	PAR										

										REPAIR BALL MARKS	
10	11	12	13	14	15	16	17	18	IN	TOTAL	HDCP	NET
											REPLACE DIVOTS	

SCORER   ATTESTED   DATE

ROUND REPORT

Date:_____

Course:_____

Time started:_____ Time finished:_____

Weather:_____

Players: _____ Strokes received: _____

              _____   _____

              _____   _____

              _____   _____

              _____

Competition details:

Singles:	_____	Greensome:	_____
Foursomes:	_____	Stableford:	_____
3-ball:	_____	Stroke-play:	_____
4-ball:	_____	Match-play:	_____

Stakes:_____

Best hole:_____

_____

Best shot:_____

_____

Incidents:_____

_____

_____

_____

Result:_____

_____

_____

_____

©

"The game is so fostered by companionship and wrapped about with the joys of friendship, that he who has his soul's friend for his golfing mate is on fortune's cap the very button. With such company, when the November wind streams down the course, whipping out our little clouds of breath into streamers, we can stride over our 18 holes with the keen joy of living that comes at intervals to the tired worker. And then, oh! weary soul, what joys await the faithful! The putting off of mud-caked shoes, the brisk plunge or shower-bath, and the warm glow thereafter; the immaculate shirt-front that crackles at your touch, the glad joy of dinner and the utter relaxation of content, "with just a wee drappie of guid Scotch to follow"."

SCRIBNER'S MAGAZINE, May 1895

MENS' OFFICIAL COURSE	PAR										
	DISTANCE										
	HANDICAP/STROKE INDEX										
A											
B											
	HOLE	1	2	3	4	5	6	7	8	9	OUT
C											
D											
MATCHES											
LADIES' OFFICIAL COURSE	HANDICAP/STROKE INDEX										
	DISTANCE										
	PAR										

										REPAIR BALL MARKS	
10	11	12	13	14	15	16	17	18	IN	TOTAL	HDCP	NET
										REPLACE DIVOTS	
SCORER		ATTESTED			DATE						

ROUND REPORT

Date: _____

Course: _____

Time started: _____ Time finished: _____

Weather: _____

Players: _____ Strokes received: _____

_____ _____

_____ _____

_____ _____

_____ _____

Competition details:

Singles: _____ Greensome: _____

Foursomes: _____ Stableford: _____

3-ball: _____ Stroke-play: _____

4-ball: _____ Match-play: _____

Stakes: _____

Best hole: _____

_____

Best shot: _____

_____

Incidents: _____

_____

_____

_____

Result: _____

_____

_____

_____

©

"The game of golf is in a fair way of becoming unplayable in America, on account of the amazing and unconscionable slowness of American players. The prevalent idea that the American is a born hustler is sadly belied on the golf links. It may be that just because he has learned to travel in express subway trains, the American has forgotten how to walk on the golf links.

But that is not the only reason why he takes such a long time to get round the course. Because Walter Travis takes a practise swing before most shots, the beginner appears to think he cannot become a good golfer unless he does the same. So he takes a preliminary swing, and then waggles his club needlessly over the ball, or crouches over it with glaring eye as if by sheer hypnotic power he would compel it to fly. As a result, it is almost impossible to get round a crowded links in less than two hours and a half."

OUTING, 1910

MENS' OFFICIAL COURSE	PAR											
	DISTANCE											
	HANDICAP/STROKE INDEX											
A												
B												
HOLE		1	2	3	4	5	6	7	8	9	OUT	
C												
D												
MATCHES												
LADIES' OFFICIAL COURSE	HANDICAP/STROKE INDEX											
	DISTANCE											
	PAR											

									REPAIR BALL MARKS	
10	11	12	13	14	15	16	17	18	IN	TOTAL	HDCP	NET
											REPLACE DIVOTS	
SCORER		ATTESTED		DATE								

©

91

ROUND REPORT

Date:_____

Course:_____

Time started:_____ Time finished:_____

Weather:_____

Players: _____ Strokes received: _____

         _____   _____

         _____   _____

         _____   _____

         _____   _____

Competition details:

Singles:	_____	Greensome:	_____
Foursomes:	_____	Stableford:	_____
3-ball:	_____	Stroke-play:	_____
4-ball:	_____	Match-play:	_____

Stakes:_____

Best hole:_____

_____

Best shot:_____

_____

Incidents:_____

_____

_____

_____

Result:_____

_____

_____

_____

©

"When you have any bit of hard luck, don't keep talking about it for several holes afterwards. In the first place, your opponent, though he may condole with you for form's sake, really does not think that you had such bad luck; if he were honest with you, he would tell you that he thinks you played the shot badly. The more you talk about such things, the more he thinks that you ae getting old and cranky and really rather a nuisance to play with. In the second place, talking about your bad luck only makes you dwell on your sorrows and tends to spoil your play. It is not true that you consistently get worse lies than other people. When a man tells you that he always holds bad cards at bridge you never think of believing him; you take him to mean that he always plays them badly."

OUTING, 1910

MENS' OFFICIAL COURSE	PAR											
	DISTANCE											
	HANDICAP/STROKE INDEX											
A												
B												
	HOLE	1	2	3	4	5	6	7	8	9	OUT	
C												
D												
MATCHES												
LADIES' OFFICIAL COURSE	HANDICAP/STROKE INDEX											
	DISTANCE											
	PAR											

											REPAIR BALL MARKS	
10	11	12	13	14	15	16	17	18	IN	TOTAL	HDCP	NET
											REPLACE DIVOTS	

SCORER	ATTESTED	DATE

ROUND REPORT

Date:_____

Course:_____

Time started:_____ Time finished:_____

Weather:_____

Players:_____ Strokes received:_____

_____   _____

_____   _____

_____   _____

_____   _____

Competition details:

      Singles:_____   Greensome:_____

      Foursomes:_____   Stableford:_____

      3-ball:_____   Stroke-play:_____

      4-ball:_____   Match-play:_____

Stakes:_____

Best hole:_____

_____

Best shot:_____

_____

Incidents:_____

_____

_____

_____

Result:_____

_____

_____

_____

©

"There is another golfing story having something of the mythical tone, which is yet so possible as to be almost credible. On a very rainy day – upon a very soft and clay-covered course – a golfer swung his club down on a ball resting on the side of a bunker. Watching to see the flight of the ball, he saw nothing. Looking at the ground, he could not see it. But, happening to notice the head of his club, he saw a large clot of clay clinging to it, in which the ball was embedded. The story goes on to say that he walked up to the hole, shook the ball out of the clay into it, claimed the hole, and it was given to him. That the first could happen is highly probable, but the climax may be questioned. Still, this is not beyond the bounds of possibility as far as the Rules are concerned."

George Hibbard, 1904

MENS' OFFICIAL COURSE	PAR											
	DISTANCE											
	HANDICAP/STROKE INDEX											
A												
B												
	HOLE	1	2	3	4	5	6	7	8	9	OUT	
C												
D												
MATCHES												
LADIES' OFFICIAL COURSE	HANDICAP/STROKE INDEX											
	DISTANCE											
	PAR											

										REPAIR BALL MARKS	
10	11	12	13	14	15	16	17	18	IN	TOTAL	HDCP	NET
										REPLACE DIVOTS	
SCORER		ATTESTED			DATE						

95

ROUND REPORT

Date: _____

Course: _____

Time started: _____ Time finished: _____

Weather: _____

Players: _____ Strokes received: _____

_____   _____

_____   _____

_____   _____

_____   _____

Competition details:

       Singles: _____   Greensome: _____

       Foursomes: _____   Stableford: _____

       3-ball: _____   Stroke-play: _____

       4-ball: _____   Match-play: _____

Stakes: _____

Best hole: _____

_____

Best shot: _____

_____

Incidents: _____

_____

_____

_____

Result: _____

_____

_____

_____

©

"Long experience upon the links teaches one to be genially tolerant of the mathematical miscalculations of others. It is a strange thing that men who invariably add up a bridge score correctly – Wall Street magnates, captains of industry, masters of finance who can tell offhand the profit they have made on 460 Canadian Pacific ordinary shares when the stock rises three points – often display a lamentable incapacity for estimating the exact number of times they have struck a golf ball between the tee and the green.

Persons of unblemished reputation and scrupulous integrity will entirely forget whether they took three or four strokes to get out of a bunker; the fact that their first drive went out of bounds, and that they were forced to play a second shot from the tee, escapes their memory in a way that non-golfers might deem incredible."

Harry Graham, THE COMPLETE SPORTSMAN, 1931

MENS' OFFICIAL COURSE	PAR										
	DISTANCE										
	HANDICAP/STROKE INDEX										
A											
B											
	HOLE	**1**	**2**	**3**	**4**	**5**	**6**	**7**	**8**	**9**	**OUT**
C											
D											
MATCHES											
LADIES' OFFICIAL COURSE	HANDICAP/STROKE INDEX										
	DISTANCE										
	PAR										

										REPAIR BALL MARKS	
10	**11**	**12**	**13**	**14**	**15**	**16**	**17**	**18**	**IN**	**TOTAL**	**HDCP**	**NET**
											REPLACE DIVOTS	
SCORER			ATTESTED					DATE				

©

ROUND REPORT

Date: _____

Course: _____

Time started: _____ Time finished: _____

Weather: _____

Players: _____ Strokes received: _____

     _____   _____

     _____   _____

     _____   _____

     _____   _____

Competition details:

    Singles: _____   Greensome: _____

    Foursomes: _____   Stableford: _____

    3-ball: _____   Stroke-play: _____

    4-ball: _____   Match-play: _____

Stakes: _____

Best hole: _____

_____

Best shot: _____

_____

Incidents: _____

_____

_____

_____

Result: _____

_____

_____

_____

©

"With the development of the game comes the development of the caddie, who is one of its principal adjuncts. In America he is still the small boy with no special peculiarites to distinguish him from others. In Scotland, he is as much of an institution as the player himself. He has grown up on the links, and is the guide, counsellor and friend of the player whose clubs he carries. One of his principal qualifications there is that he should be able to conceal his contempt for your game. He is ready with advice, reproof, criticism and sympathy, always interested, ready at critical times with the appropriate club, and, if need be, with the appropriate comment. He is anxious for the success of his side as if he were one of the players. His caustic remarks are borne with equanimity, and his contemptuous criticisms with the submission they deserve."

SCRIBNER'S MAGAZINE, May 1895

MENS' OFFICIAL COURSE	PAR										
	DISTANCE										
	HANDICAP/STROKE INDEX										
A											
B											
HOLE		1	2	3	4	5	6	7	8	9	OUT
C											
D											
MATCHES											
LADIES' OFFICIAL COURSE	HANDICAP/STROKE INDEX										
	DISTANCE										
	PAR										

10	11	12	13	14	15	16	17	18	IN	TOTAL	HDCP	NET
											REPAIR BALL MARKS	
											REPLACE DIVOTS	
SCORER		ATTESTED					DATE					

ROUND REPORT

Date:_____

Course:_____

Time started:_____ Time finished:_____

Weather:_____

Players: _____ Strokes received: _____

_____ _____

_____ _____

_____ _____

_____ _____

Competition details:

Singles: _____   Greensome: _____

Foursomes: _____   Stableford: _____

3-ball: _____   Stroke-play: _____

4-ball: _____   Match-play: _____

Stakes:_____

Best hole:_____

_____

Best shot:_____

_____

Incidents:_____

_____

_____

_____

Result:_____

_____

_____

_____

©

"A Scotch proverb says, "He who plays with a thistle must expect to get pricked", and he who plays golf must expect to get into trouble. Indeed, a golfer's life is one continuous series of problems: "How to get out of trouble".

Trouble he will have, willy-nilly. This may at the first blush seem a somewhat dispiriting view to take of so fascinating a game, but it is the very variety of the points of the game, ever occurring yet scarcely ever duplicated, that gives it its unique position. It is this that renders it so exhilarating to the devotee, both mentally and physically."

OUTING, August 1898

MENS' OFFICIAL COURSE	PAR										
	DISTANCE										
	HANDICAP/STROKE INDEX										
A											
B											
	HOLE	1	2	3	4	5	6	7	8	9	OUT
C											
D											
MATCHES											
LADIES' OFFICIAL COURSE	HANDICAP/STROKE INDEX										
	DISTANCE										
	PAR										

										REPAIR BALL MARKS	
10	11	12	13	14	15	16	17	18	IN	TOTAL	HDCP	NET
											REPLACE DIVOTS	
SCORER		ATTESTED		DATE							

ROUND REPORT

Date: _____

Course: _____

Time started: _____ Time finished: _____

Weather: _____

Players: _____ Strokes received: _____

                   _____   _____

                   _____   _____

                   _____   _____

                   _____   _____

Competition details:

Singles:	_____	Greensome:	_____
Foursomes:	_____	Stableford:	_____
3-ball:	_____	Stroke-play:	_____
4-ball:	_____	Match-play:	_____

Stakes: _____

Best hole: _____

_____

Best shot: _____

_____

Incidents: _____

_____

_____

_____

Result: _____

_____

_____

_____

©

"Egotism is powerless to excuse a fault, for that can lie only with the player himself. He cannot vent his fury upon an opponent, even though a tree opportunely situated may land a ball on the green, while his own flies hopelessly into the woods; for the game is born in the purple of equable temper and courtesy, and the golfer's expletives must be directed against his own lack of skill, or lies, or hazards, and the luck and vengeance must light, and often do, on the un-offending clubs, even to their utter extermination. To the language with which every golf course is strewn, differing more in form than in substance, from the "Tut, tut, tut" of the ecclesiastic to the more sulphurous exclamation of the layman, the divine quality of forgiveness must be extended."

SCRIBNER'S MAGAZINE, May 1895

MENS' OFFICIAL COURSE	PAR										
	DISTANCE										
	HANDICAP/STROKE INDEX										
A											
B											
	HOLE	1	2	3	4	5	6	7	8	9	OUT
C											
D											
MATCHES											
	HANDICAP/STROKE INDEX										
LADIES' OFFICIAL COURSE	DISTANCE										
	PAR										

									REPAIR BALL MARKS	
10	11	12	13	14	15	16	17	18	IN	TOTAL	HDCP	NET
											REPLACE DIVOTS	
SCORER			ATTESTED				DATE					

ROUND REPORT

Date:_____

Course:_____

Time started:_____ Time finished:_____

Weather:_____

Players:_____ Strokes received:_____

_____ _____

_____ _____

_____ _____

_____ _____

Competition details:

Singles:_____ Greensome:_____

Foursomes:_____ Stableford:_____

3-ball:_____ Stroke-play:_____

4-ball:_____ Match-play:_____

Stakes:_____

Best hole:_____

_____

Best shot:_____

_____

Incidents:_____

_____

_____

_____

Result:_____

_____

_____

_____

©

"It is an essential characteristic of the true golfer that he should be able to praise an opponent's good strokes and sympathize with his bad ones in a natural and whole-hearted fashion, and at the shortest possible notice. When he is four down at the turn, and his adversary lays his second shot dead, or when his rival's drive drops like a stone into a bunker, it is no easy task to exclaim "Well played!" or "Bad luck!" (as the case may be) in tones that carry conviction. "In thinking of the sorrows of others," as a great philosopher once remarked, "we forget our own," and the truth of this saying is nowhere more apparent than on the golf-links."

Harry Graham, THE COMPLETE SPORTSMAN, 1931

MENS' OFFICIAL COURSE	PAR										
	DISTANCE										
	HANDICAP / STROKE INDEX										
A											
B											
	HOLE	1	2	3	4	5	6	7	8	9	OUT
C											
D											
MATCHES											
LADIES' OFFICIAL COURSE	HANDICAP / STROKE INDEX										
	DISTANCE										
	PAR										

								REPAIR BALL MARKS	
10	11	12	13	14	15	16	17	18	IN	TOTAL	HDCP	NET
										REPLACE DIVOTS	
SCORER		ATTESTED			DATE				

ROUND REPORT

Date: _____

Course: _____

Time started: _____ Time finished: _____

Weather: _____

Players: _____ Strokes received: _____

                        _____   _____

                        _____   _____

                        _____   _____

                        _____   _____

Competition details:

Singles:	_____		Greensome:	_____
Foursomes:	_____		Stableford:	_____
3-ball:	_____		Stroke-play:	_____
4-ball:	_____		Match-play:	_____

Stakes: _____

Best hole: _____

_____

Best shot: _____

_____

Incidents: _____

_____

_____

_____

Result: _____

_____

_____

_____

©

"The finest round of golf Bobby Jones ever played was over the Old Course of the Sunningdale Golf Club, in Surrey, not far from London; his first of two rounds, qualifying for the British Open Championship of 1926. Mr Bernard Darwin said at the time it was the finest round ever played in Britain. So far as I know, and assuredly so far as I have observed, there never was one to compare with it in America.

There have been lower-scoring rounds – Bobby has scored better himself – though I do not recall a card as good connected with a major championship at medal play. The point is, this score of 66 was registered by almost perfect golf, played with a precision and a freedom from error never attained before or since by the greatest precisionist of all."

OB Keeler, A BOY'S LIFE OF BOBBY JONES, 1931

MENS' OFFICIAL COURSE	PAR										
	DISTANCE										
	HANDICAP/STROKE INDEX										
A											
B											
	HOLE	1	2	3	4	5	6	7	8	9	OUT
C											
D											
MATCHES											
LADIES' OFFICIAL COURSE	HANDICAP/STROKE INDEX										
	DISTANCE										
	PAR										

										REPAIR BALL MARKS	
10	11	12	13	14	15	16	17	18	IN	TOTAL	HDCP	NET
											REPLACE DIVOTS	
SCORER		ATTESTED		DATE							

©

ROUND REPORT

Date:_____

Course:_____

Time started:_____ Time finished:_____

Weather:_____

Players: _____ Strokes received: _____

        _____   _____

        _____   _____

        _____   _____

        _____   _____

Competition details:

Singles:	_____	Greensome:	_____
Foursomes:	_____	Stableford:	_____
3-ball:	_____	Stroke-play:	_____
4-ball:	_____	Match-play:	_____

Stakes:_____

Best hole:_____
_____

Best shot:_____
_____

Incidents:_____
_____
_____
_____

Result:_____
_____
_____
_____

©

108

"For a long time, I believed that the tale of a bird killed by a golf ball was apocryphal. The first convincing testimony came from an acquaintance. A bird had been killed by a golf ball – to his knowledge. And, most remarkable of all, a flying bird by a golf ball also soaring through the air. The driven ball struck the bird fairly, and it fell dead. That there can be doubt about this, I hasten to give the reasons for my confidence. The fact is attested by a distinguished divine of the Presbyterian Church, and a Judge of the Court of Appeals of the State of New York, than which, as any one must admit, there could not be better testimony. Usually and historical occurrence does not take place under such fortunate conditions."

George Hibbard, 1904

MENS' OFFICIAL COURSE	PAR										
	DISTANCE										
	HANDICAP/STROKE INDEX										
A											
B											
	HOLE	1	2	3	4	5	6	7	8	9	OUT
C											
D											
MATCHES											
LADIES' OFFICIAL COURSE	HANDICAP/STROKE INDEX										
	DISTANCE										
	PAR										

										REPAIR BALL MARKS	
10	11	12	13	14	15	16	17	18	IN	TOTAL	HDCP	NET
										REPLACE DIVOTS	

| SCORER | ATTESTED | DATE |

©

ROUND REPORT

Date:_____

Course:_____

Time started:_____ Time finished:_____

Weather:_____

Players:_____ Strokes received:_____

_____ _____

_____ _____

_____ _____

_____ _____

Competition details:

      Singles:_____   Greensome:_____

      Foursomes:_____   Stableford:_____

      3-ball:_____   Stroke-play:_____

      4-ball:_____   Match-play:_____

Stakes:_____

Best hole:_____

_____

Best shot:_____

_____

Incidents:_____

_____

_____

_____

Result:_____

_____

_____

_____

©

"Golfers as a rule are an exceptionally honest race of men, but uncertain arithmetic is occasionally encountered on the green. "I aim to tell the truth," said one; "Well, you are a very bad shot," was the reply, and there is often an area of low veracity about a bunker. Accuracy is a cardinal virtue in the game, and a kindly judgement may attribute such errors to forgetfulness; but as the chief pleasure is to beat your own record for your own satisfaction, and as this form of deception makes real progress continually more difficult, for the discount is always in your path, the man of treacherous memory gets small comfort out of his duplicity."

SCRIBNER'S MAGAZINE, May 1895

MENS' OFFICIAL COURSE	PAR										
	DISTANCE										
	HANDICAP/STROKE INDEX										
A											
B											
HOLE		**1**	**2**	**3**	**4**	**5**	**6**	**7**	**8**	**9**	**OUT**
C											
D											
MATCHES											
LADIES' OFFICIAL COURSE	HANDICAP/STROKE INDEX										
	DISTANCE										
	PAR										

										REPAIR BALL MARKS	
10	**11**	**12**	**13**	**14**	**15**	**16**	**17**	**18**	**IN**	**TOTAL**	**HDCP**	**NET**
											REPLACE DIVOTS	

| SCORER | ATTESTED | DATE |

©

ROUND REPORT

Date: _____

Course: _____

Time started: _____ Time finished: _____

Weather: _____

Players: _____ Strokes received: _____

_____ _____

_____ _____

_____ _____

_____ _____

Competition details:

Singles:	_____	Greensome:	_____
Foursomes:	_____	Stableford:	_____
3-ball:	_____	Stroke-play:	_____
4-ball:	_____	Match-play:	_____

Stakes: _____

Best hole: _____

_____

Best shot: _____

_____

Incidents: _____

_____

_____

_____

Result: _____

_____

_____

_____

©

"Golf is like a patent medicine; it either kills or cures. If you realize at the beginning that to be a good golfer you must, before all things, control your temper, you will find after a while that it is just as easy to be cheerful as not and a great deal more pleasant. And the result of this schooling of the temper is that you are a better and more lovable person in all relations of life.

But if you once begin getting angry and morose at golf, you will rapidly become worse and worse until there is no playing with you or living with you. So be warned in time. When you top a drive into a bunker or miss a short putt, remember that you are playing the game for amusement, even if you are desperately keen to win. Tell yourself that your only hope of winning lies in forgetting past errors."

OUTING, 1910

MENS' OFFICIAL COURSE	PAR										
	DISTANCE										
	HANDICAP/STROKE INDEX										
A											
B											
	HOLE	1	2	3	4	5	6	7	8	9	OUT
C											
D											
MATCHES											
LADIES' OFFICIAL COURSE	HANDICAP/STROKE INDEX										
	DISTANCE										
	PAR										

											REPAIR BALL MARKS	
10	11	12	13	14	15	16	17	18	IN	TOTAL	HDCP	NET
											REPLACE DIVOTS	
SCORER		ATTESTED			DATE							

©

ROUND REPORT

Date: _____

Course: _____

Time started: _____ Time finished: _____

Weather: _____

Players: _____ Strokes received: _____

_____ _____

_____ _____

_____ _____

_____ _____

Competition details:

Singles:	_____	Greensome:	_____
Foursomes:	_____	Stableford:	_____
3-ball:	_____	Stroke-play:	_____
4-ball:	_____	Match-play:	_____

Stakes: _____

Best hole: _____

_____

Best shot: _____

_____

Incidents: _____

_____

_____

_____

Result: _____

_____

_____

_____

©

"The influence of golf upon dogs, as upon their nominal owners, has been almost purely beneficial. Almost …

In June 1899, a touching story was told of the links where one of the club pets was a smart fox terrier. The third hole was blind: but the number of balls disappearing there was inexplicable. More often than not, the search for them was abandoned; but at the 11th hole, a dear little girl was generally ready to offer, with pretty shyness, some nice clean balls, which the players would be charmed to buy. The sweet child, as it turned out, lived in the same cottage as the dog.

Then, in last year's *Scotsman*, we read a cruel and wickedly casual reference to a Mr Hislop, who is said to have had a famous terrier called *Prince*, which he had trained to push his opponent's ball into the burn."

GOLF MONTHLY, March 1912

MENS' OFFICIAL COURSE	PAR										
	DISTANCE										
	HANDICAP/STROKE INDEX										
A											
B											
	HOLE	1	2	3	4	5	6	7	8	9	OUT
C											
D											
MATCHES											
LADIES' OFFICIAL COURSE	HANDICAP/STROKE INDEX										
	DISTANCE										
	PAR										

											REPAIR BALL MARKS
10	11	12	13	14	15	16	17	18	IN	TOTAL	HDCP	NET
											REPLACE DIVOTS

| SCORER | ATTESTED | DATE |

ROUND REPORT

Date: _____

Course: _____

Time started: _____ Time finished: _____

Weather: _____

Players: _____ Strokes received: _____

_____ _____

_____ _____

_____ _____

_____ _____

Competition details:

Singles: _____ Greensome: _____

Foursomes: _____ Stableford: _____

3-ball: _____ Stroke-play: _____

4-ball: _____ Match-play: _____

Stakes: _____

Best hole: _____

_____

Best shot: _____

_____

Incidents: _____

_____

_____

_____

Result: _____

_____

_____

_____

©

"The fascinations of golf can only be learned by experience. It is difficult to explain them. It has its humorous and its serious side. It can be begun as soon as you walk, and once begun it is continued as long as you can see. The very nature of the exercise gives length of days. Freedom of movement, swing of shoulder, and that suppleness of which the glory had departed, all return to the enthusiast. He has a confidence in his own ability which is sublime, because it is justified by performance, and that self-control which chafes the ordinary adversary. His sense of the ultimate purpose and the true proportions of his existence in unruffled ... his soul is so wrapped in the harmony of earth and sky and the glory of the game that no buffets of fortune can come at him."

SCRIBNER'S MAGAZINE, May 1895

MENS' OFFICIAL COURSE	PAR										
	DISTANCE										
	HANDICAP/STROKE INDEX										
A											
B											
	HOLE	1	2	3	4	5	6	7	8	9	OUT
C											
D											
MATCHES											
LADIES' OFFICIAL COURSE	HANDICAP/STROKE INDEX										
	DISTANCE										
	PAR										

									REPAIR BALL MARKS	
10	11	12	13	14	15	16	17	18	IN	TOTAL	HDCP	NET
											REPLACE DIVOTS	

| SCORER | ATTESTED | DATE |

Round Report

Date: _____

Course: _____

Time started: _____ Time finished: _____

Weather: _____

Players: _____ Strokes received: _____

       _____   _____

       _____   _____

       _____   _____

       _____   _____

Competition details:

Singles:	_____	Greensome:	_____
Foursomes:	_____	Stableford:	_____
3-ball:	_____	Stroke-play:	_____
4-ball:	_____	Match-play:	_____

Stakes: _____

Best hole: _____

_____

Best shot: _____

_____

Incidents: _____

_____

_____

_____

Result: _____

_____

_____

_____

©

"The man who prides himself upon his long, albeit erratic, driving is apt to think himself badly treated if a long pulled ball finds itself safely tucked away in a pot-bunker. Nevertheless, his grounds for complaint are untenable. Golf is a game in which brains should play a part at least as important with that of the physical organization. In the old days, if a player happened to strike an unusually clean hit ball, with a following wind, and so reached a cross-bunker intended, under ordinary circumstances, for the second shot, he then considered he had the right to drop back without penalty; generally there was a local rule that allowed him to do so. Now we realize that a true golfer adapts his game to changing conditions, and avoids the penalty of overplay by using a less powerful club."

THE YEAR IN GOLF, 1906

MENS' OFFICIAL COURSE	PAR										
	DISTANCE										
	HANDICAP/STROKE INDEX										
A											
B											
	HOLE	1	2	3	4	5	6	7	8	9	OUT
C											
D											
MATCHES											
LADIES' OFFICIAL COURSE	HANDICAP/STROKE INDEX										
	DISTANCE										
	PAR										

										REPAIR BALL MARKS	
10	11	12	13	14	15	16	17	18	IN	TOTAL	HDCP	NET
										REPLACE DIVOTS	

| SCORER | ATTESTED | DATE |

©

ROUND REPORT

Date:_____

Course:_____

Time started:_____ Time finished:_____

Weather:_____

Players: _____ Strokes received: _____

        _____   _____

        _____   _____

        _____   _____

        _____   _____

Competition details:

        Singles: _____   Greensome: _____

        Foursomes: _____   Stableford: _____

        3-ball: _____   Stroke-play:_____

        4-ball: _____   Match-play:_____

Stakes:_____

Best hole:_____

_____

Best shot:_____

_____

Incidents:_____

_____

_____

_____

Result:_____

_____

_____

_____

©

"It is easily to be understood that the natural inclination of all golfers, be they good, bad or indifferent, is to favour the club which gives them the most satisfaction. It may be a driver, a brassey, or an iron. It is indeed pleasant to take out such a club and play half a dozen balls with unerring accuracy, to see them soar away in the distance or drop, one after another, in the vicinity of the spot to which you intended them to go; but beyond that feeling of satisfaction and pleasure it profits you nothing. You knew previously that you were a master, or a comparative master, of that particular weapon, and the pleasant time spent has probably only had the object of endorsing that knowledge. Better leave your favourite club at home and take out some obstinate wretch of an instrument over which you have little or no control."

Harold H Hilton, 1900

MENS' OFFICIAL COURSE	PAR										
	DISTANCE										
	HANDICAP/STROKE INDEX										
A											
B											
	HOLE	1	2	3	4	5	6	7	8	9	OUT
C											
D											
MATCHES											
LADIES' OFFICIAL COURSE	HANDICAP/STROKE INDEX										
	DISTANCE										
	PAR										

									REPAIR BALL MARKS	
10	11	12	13	14	15	16	17	18	IN	TOTAL	HDCP	NET
										REPLACE DIVOTS	
SCORER		ATTESTED		DATE						

ROUND REPORT

Date: _____

Course: _____

Time started: _____ Time finished: _____

Weather: _____

Players: _____ Strokes received: _____

_____ _____

_____ _____

_____ _____

_____ _____

Competition details:

Singles:	_____	Greensome:	_____
Foursomes:	_____	Stableford:	_____
3-ball:	_____	Stroke-play:	_____
4-ball:	_____	Match-play:	_____

Stakes: _____

Best hole: _____

_____

Best shot: _____

_____

Incidents: _____

_____

_____

_____

Result: _____

_____

_____

_____

©

"But who shall tell of the unrecognized styles, the hooking, slicing, heeling, toeing, foozling of the would-be golfer in his game of eternal hope and everlasting despair, of bright anticipation tempered by experience, playing as if he owned the green instead of using it, cutting out divots of turf, ploughing the waste spaces, larding the green earth as he walks along, plunging down the escarpments of a hazard and keeping the recording angel busy during his sojourn there, driving into those in front, and passed on the green by succeeding players –

While those behind cry forward
And those before cry back

Let kindly forgetfulness draw a veil over this stage of his career."

SCRIBNER'S MAGAZINE, May 1895

MENS' OFFICIAL COURSE	PAR										
	DISTANCE										
	HANDICAP/STROKE INDEX										
A											
B											
HOLE		1	2	3	4	5	6	7	8	9	OUT
C											
D											
MATCHES											
LADIES' OFFICIAL COURSE	HANDICAP/STROKE INDEX										
	DISTANCE										
	PAR										

											REPAIR BALL MARKS	
10	11	12	13	14	15	16	17	18	IN	TOTAL	HDCP	NET
											REPLACE DIVOTS	
SCORER		ATTESTED			DATE							

©

COURSE REPORTS

My home course:_____

Best holes:_____

_____

Comments:_____

_____

_____

My other courses:_____

Best holes:_____

_____

Comments:_____

_____

_____

　　Phone no:_____

My other courses:_____

Best holes:_____

_____

Comments:_____

_____

_____

　　Phone no:_____

My other courses:_____

Best holes:_____

_____

Comments:_____

_____

_____

　　Phone no:_____

©

My other courses:_____

Best holes:_____

_____

Comments:_____

_____

_____

My other courses:_____

Best holes:_____

_____

Comments:_____

_____

_____

    Phone no:_____

My other courses:_____

Best holes:_____

_____

Comments:_____

_____

_____

    Phone no:_____

My other courses:_____

Best holes:_____

_____

Comments:_____

_____

_____

    Phone no:_____

MY HOME COURSE ECLECTIC

HOLES	LENGTH	PAR	CLUBS USED	DATE	SCORE	CLUBS USED	DATE	SCORE	CLUBS USED	DATE	SCORE	CLUBS USED	DATE	SCORE	BEST SCORE	
1																
2																
3																
4																
5																
6																
7																
8																
9																
OUT																
10																
11																
12																
13																
14																
15																
16																
17																
18																
IN																
TOTAL																
GROSS																
H/CAP																
NETT																

HOLES	LENGTH	PAR	CLUBS USED	DATE	SCORE	CLUBS USED	DATE	SCORE	CLUBS USED	DATE	SCORE	CLUBS USED	DATE	SCORE	BEST SCORE	
1																
2																
3																
4																
5																
6																
7																
8																
9																
OUT																
10																
11																
12																
13																
14																
15																
16																
17																
18																
IN																
TOTAL																
GROSS																
H/CAP																
NETT																

HOLES	LENGTH	PAR	CLUBS USED	DATE	SCORE	CLUBS USED	DATE	SCORE	CLUBS USED	DATE	SCORE	CLUBS USED	DATE	SCORE	BEST SCORE	
1																
2																
3																
4																
5																
6																
7																
8																
9																
OUT																
10																
11																
12																
13																
14																
15																
16																
17																
18																
IN																
TOTAL																
GROSS																
H/CAP																
NETT																

HOLES	LENGTH	PAR	CLUBS USED	DATE	SCORE	CLUBS USED	DATE	SCORE	CLUBS USED	DATE	SCORE	CLUBS USED	DATE	SCORE	BEST SCORE	
1																
2																
3																
4																
5																
6																
7																
8																
9																
OUT																
10																
11																
12																
13																
14																
15																
16																
17																
18																
IN																
TOTAL																
GROSS																
H/CAP																
NETT																

©

The GOLFER'S "IF"

With acknowledgments to
Mr. Kipling's more famous Poem.

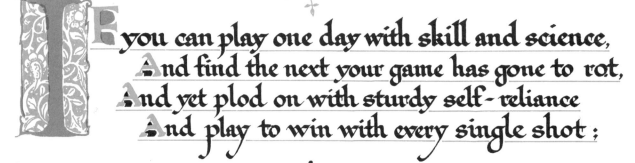

IF you can play one day with skill and science,
And find the next your game has gone to rot,
And yet plod on with sturdy self-reliance
And play to win with every single shot;

IF you can take the turf and open air way
To clear the cobwebs from a worried brain;
If, with a lie in rough or on the fairway,
You simply do your best and don't complain;

IF you can see your faults and toil to mend them,
Knowing the only mender must be you;
If you can try the wrong ways and transcend them
And when you've found the right one, Follow Through:

IN short, if head and eye do all the ruling,
With temper left discarded on the shelf,
You've got the basis of a golfer's schooling—
And not so bad a stance for Life itself.

"Peter Niblick".

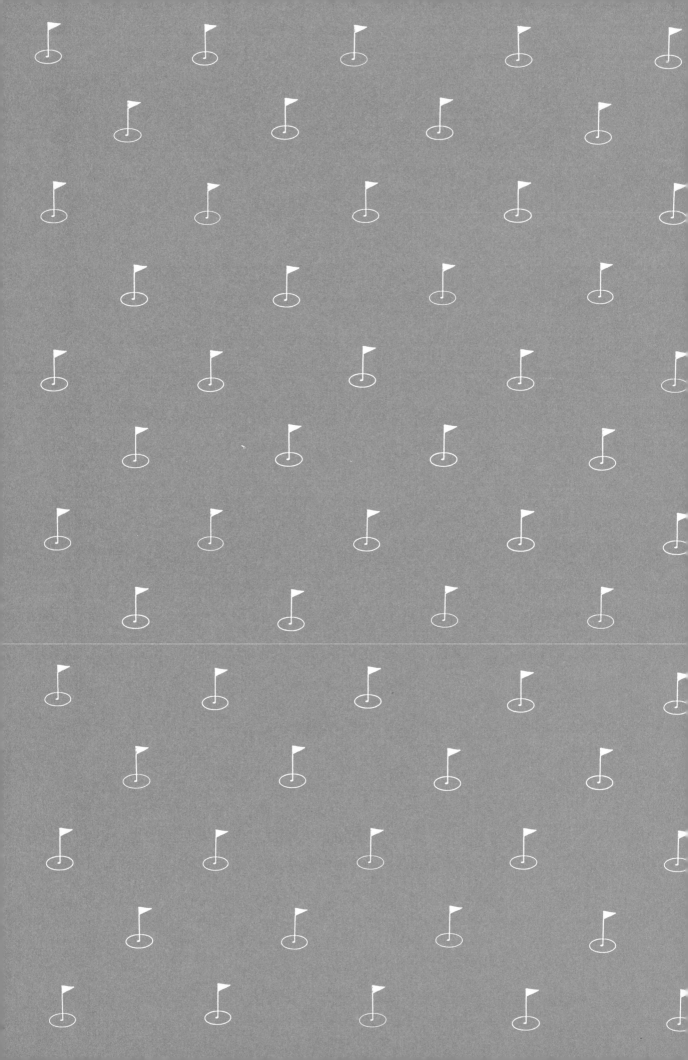